ANY DREAM WILL DO
from JOSEPH AND THE AMAZING TECHNICOLOR® DREAMCOAT

Music by ANDREW LLOYD WEBBER
Lyrics by TIM RICE

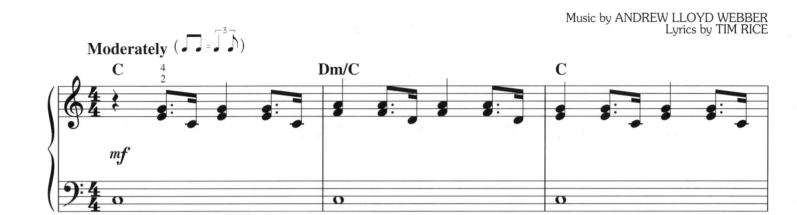

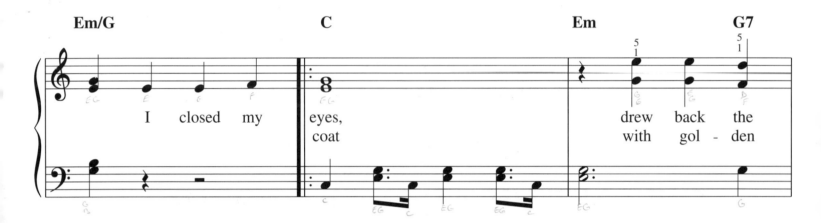

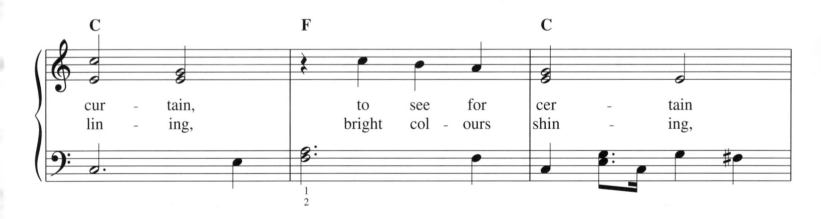

BROADWAY SONGS
EASY PIANO

HAL LEONARD EUROPE
Distributed by Music Sales

Exclusive Distributors:
Music Sales Limited
8/9 Frith Street, London W1D 3JB, England.
Music Sales Pty Limited
120 Rothschild Avenue, Rosebery, NSW 2018, Australia.

Order No. HLE90001267
ISBN 0-7119-8703-3
This book © Copyright 2002 by Hal Leonard Europe

Cover design by Michael Bell Design.
Cover photograph (Les Misérables) courtesy of Rex Features.
Printed in the USA.

Your Guarantee of Quality
As publishers, we strive to produce every book to the highest commercial standards.
The book has been carefully designed to minimise awkward page turns
and to make playing from it a real pleasure.
Throughout, the printing and binding have been planned to ensure a sturdy,
attractive publication which should give years of enjoyment.
If your copy fails to meet our high standards, please inform us and we will gladly replace it.

www.musicsales.com

out of sight,___ the col - ours fad - ed in - to dark - ness,

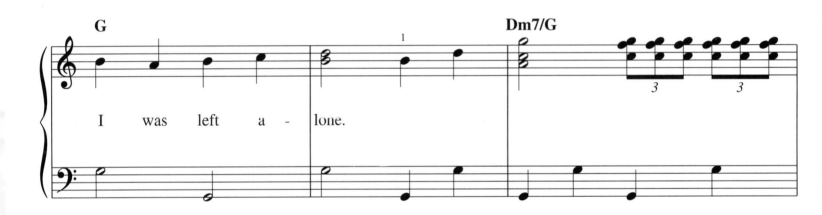

I was left a - lone.

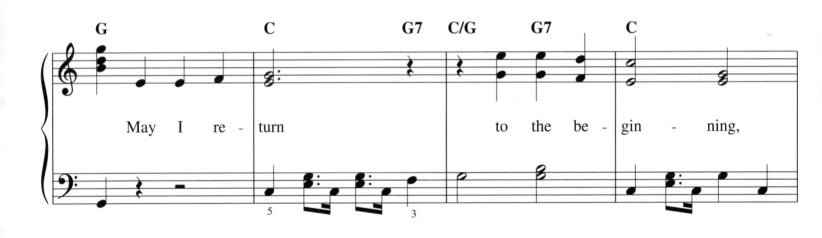

May I re - turn to the be - gin - ning,

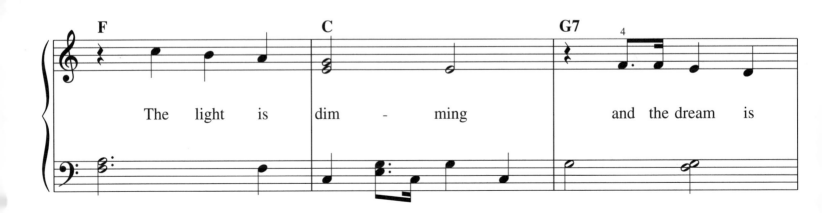

The light is dim - ming and the dream is

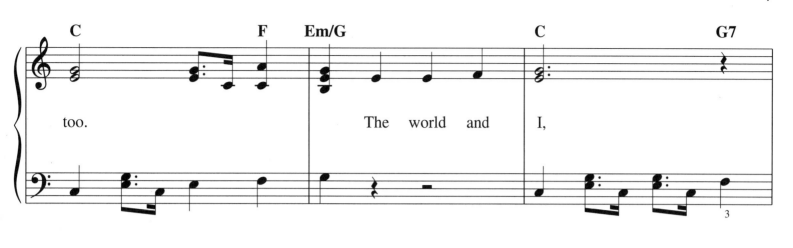

too. The world and I,

we are still wait - ing, still hes - i -

ta - ting, an - y dream will do,

an - y dream will do.

BEAUTY AND THE BEAST

from Walt Disney's BEAUTY AND THE BEAST: THE BROADWAY MUSICAL

Lyrics by HOWARD ASHMAN
Music by ALAN MENKEN

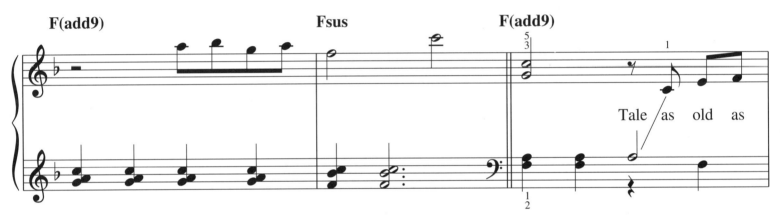

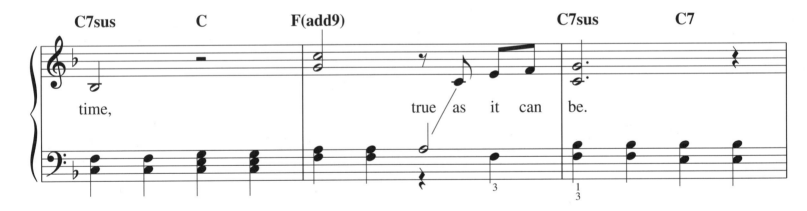

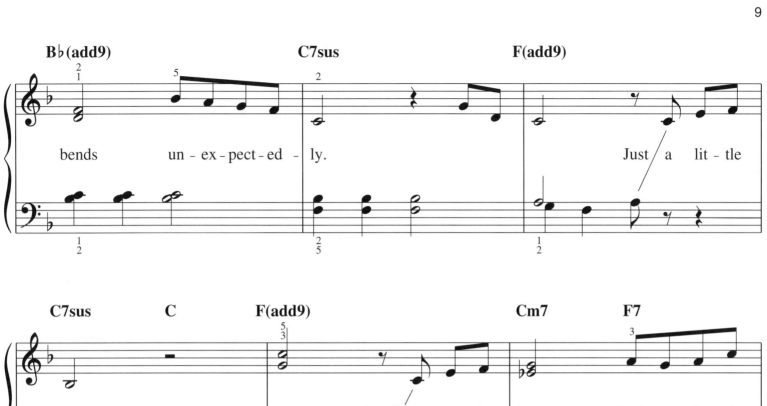

bends   un - ex - pect - ed - ly.   Just   a   lit - tle

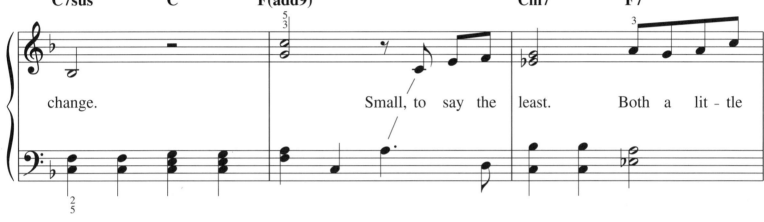

change.   Small, to say the least.   Both   a   lit - tle

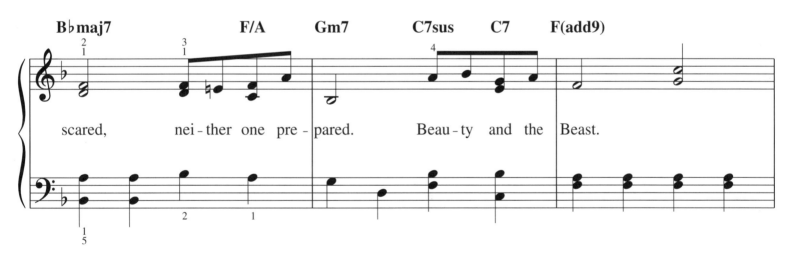

scared,   nei - ther one pre - pared.   Beau - ty   and the   Beast.

Ev - er just the   same.   Ev - er   a   sur -

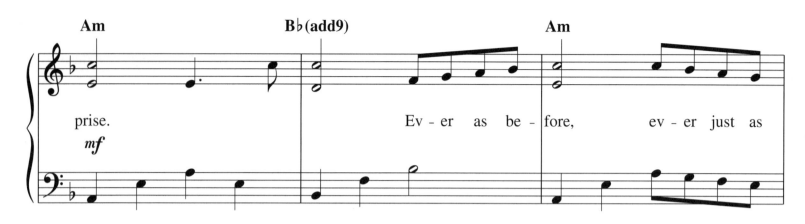

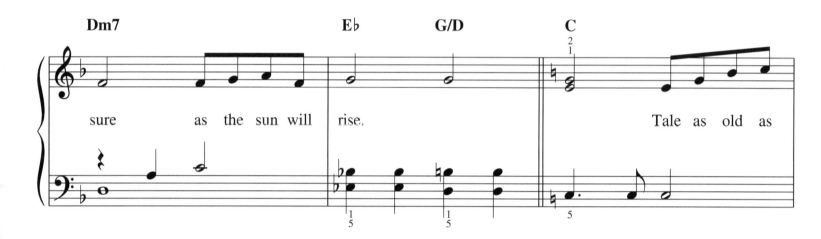

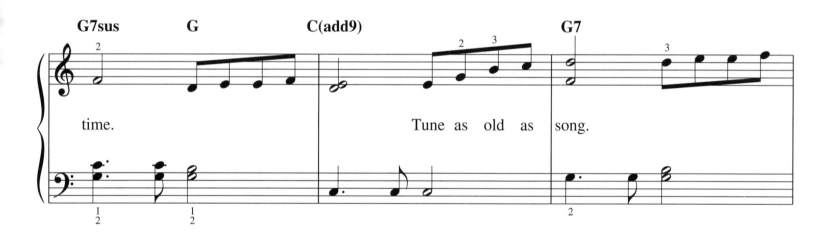

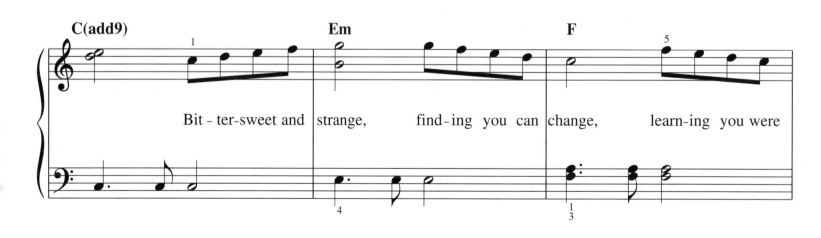

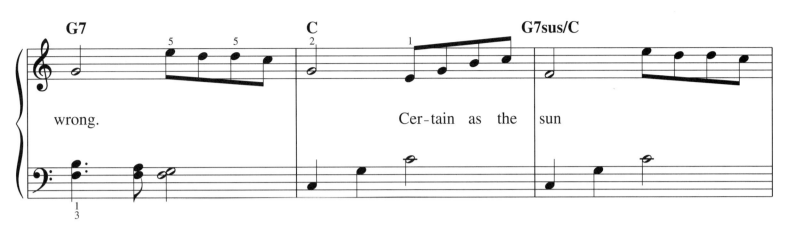

wrong.

Cer-tain as the sun rising in the

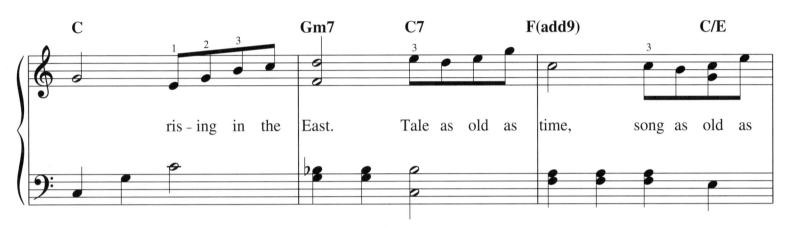

ris - ing in the East.   Tale as old as time,   song as old as

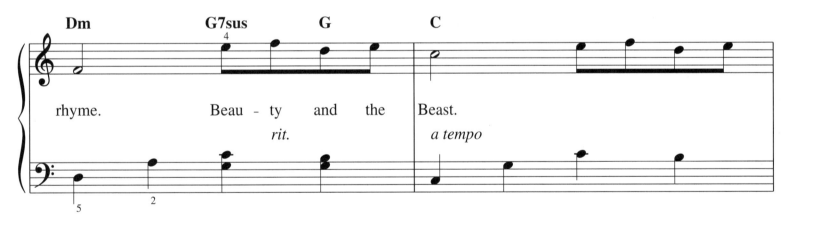

rhyme.   Beau - ty   and   the   Beast.

rit.   *a tempo*

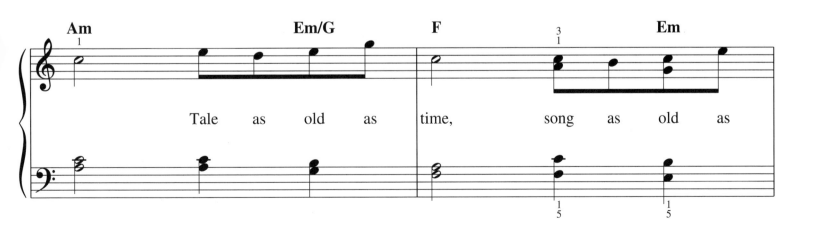

Tale   as   old   as   time,   song   as   old   as

rhyme.   Beau – ty   and   the   Beast.

BRING HIM HOME
from LES MISÉRABLES

Music by CLAUDE-MICHEL SCHÖNBERG
Lyrics by HERBERT KRETZMER and ALAIN BOUBLIL

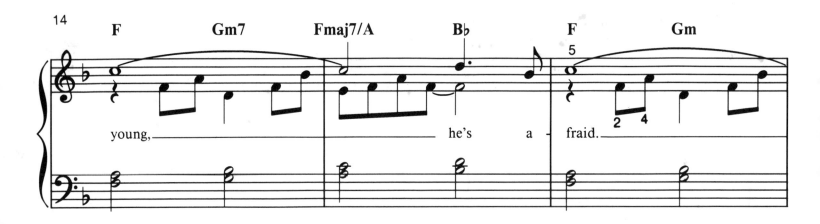

young, _____ he's a - fraid. _____

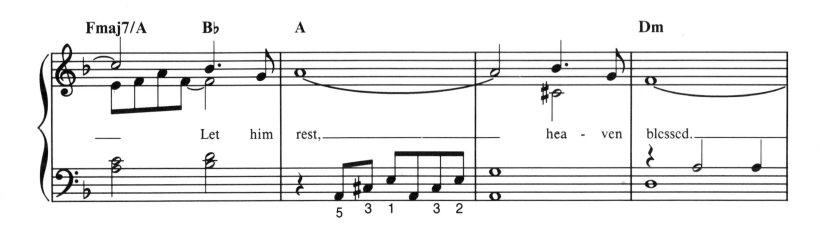

_____ Let him rest, _____ hea - ven blessed. _____

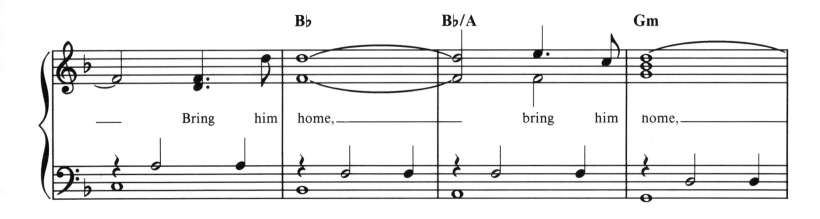

_____ Bring him home, _____ bring him home, _____

A bit faster

_____ bring him home. He's like the son I might have known

if God had grant-ed me a son. The sum-mers die one by

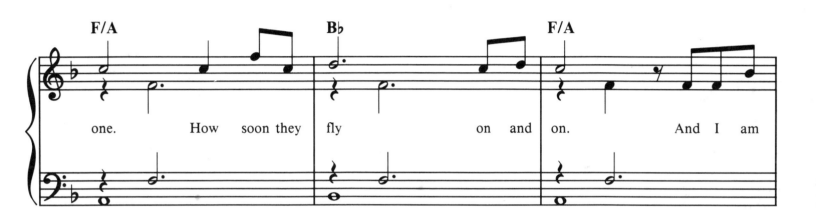

one. How soon they fly on and on. And I am

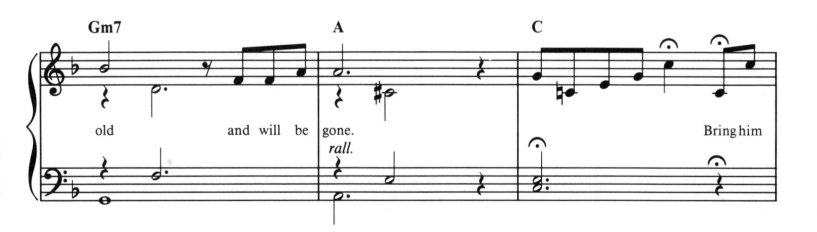

old and will be gone.
rall.
Bring him

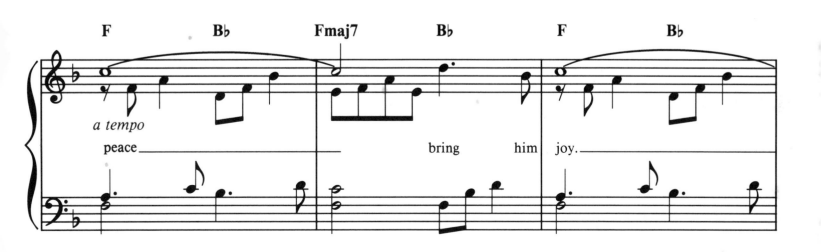

a tempo
peace_____ bring him joy._____

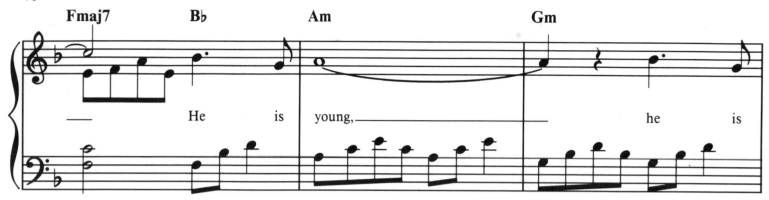

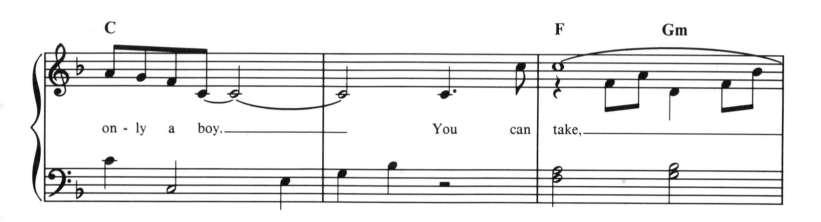

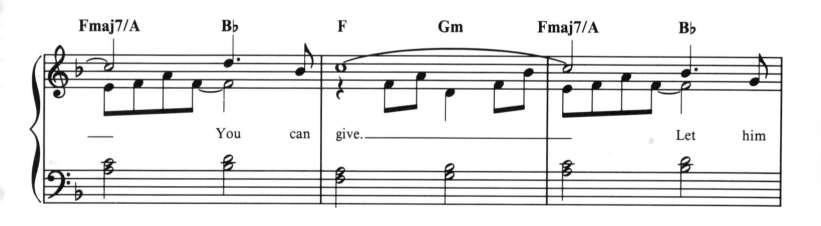

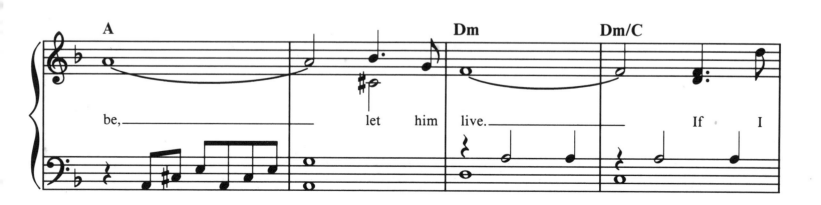

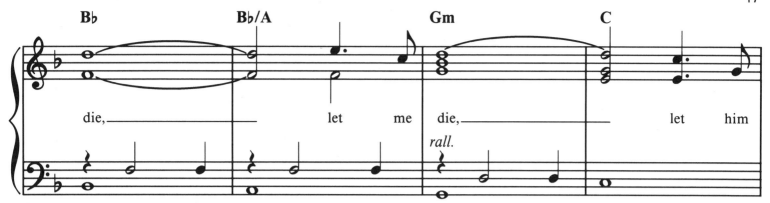

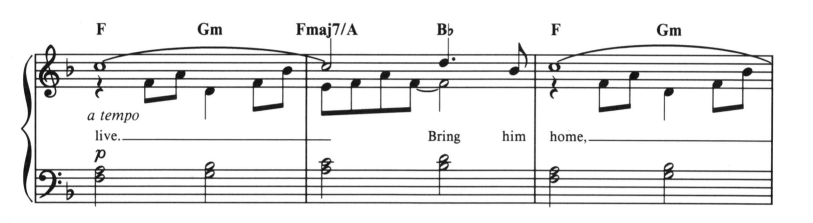

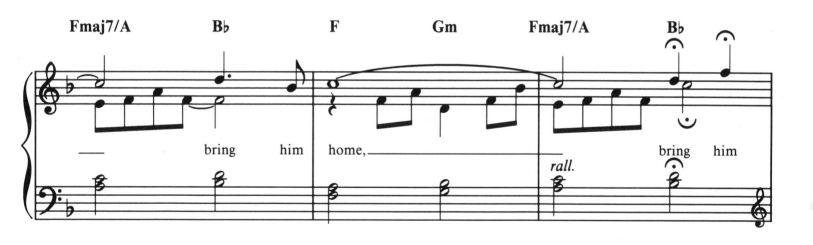

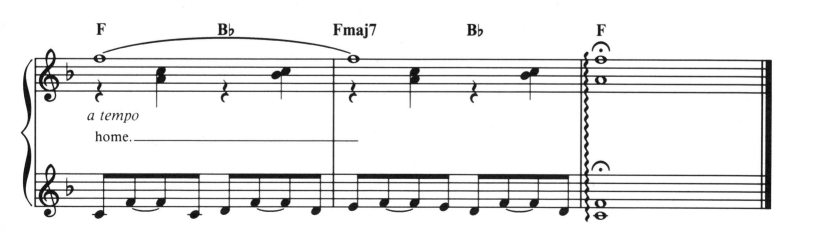

CABARET
from the Musical CABARET

Words by FRED EBB
Music by JOHN KANDER

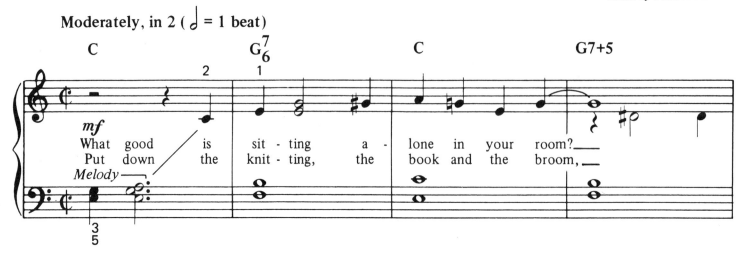

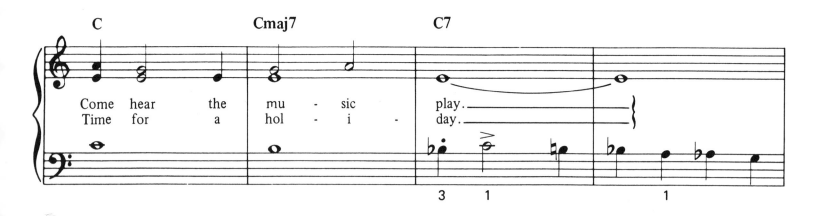

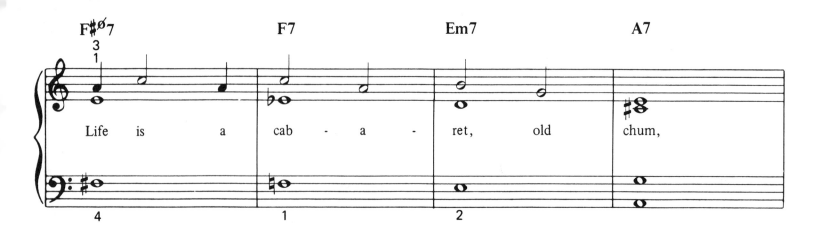

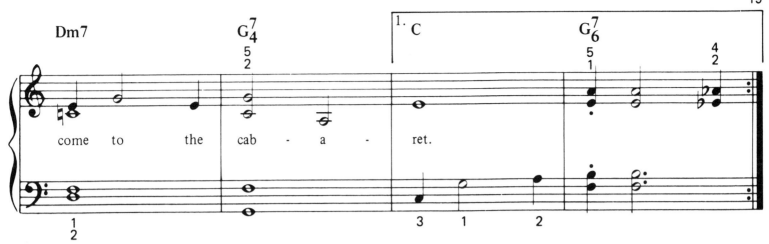

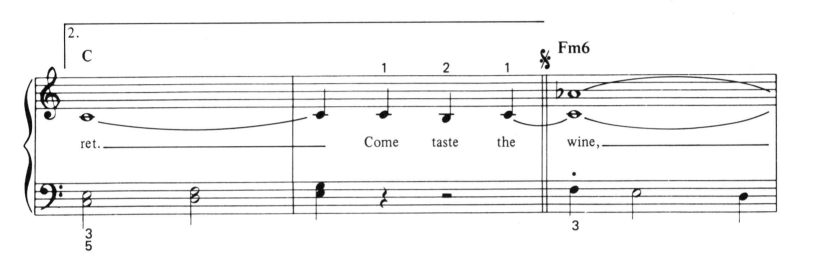

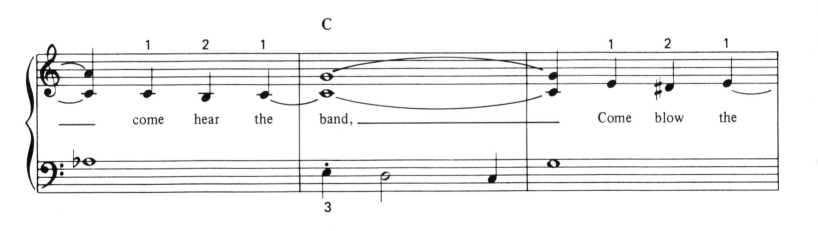

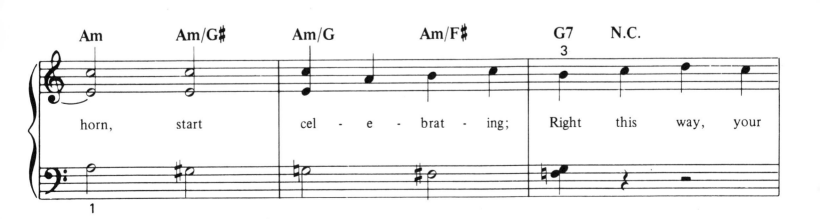

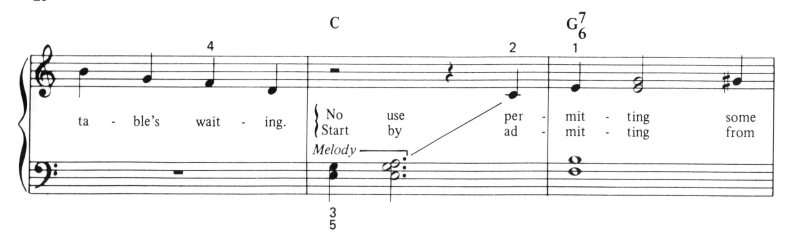

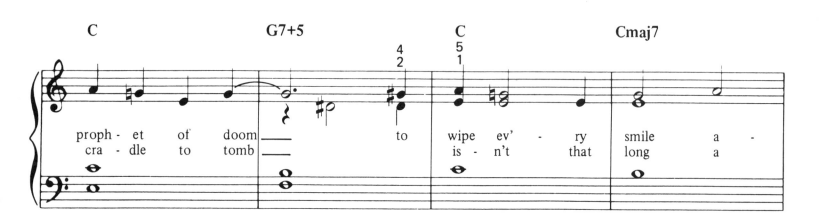

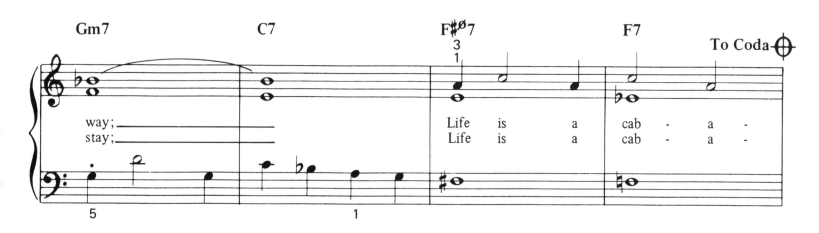

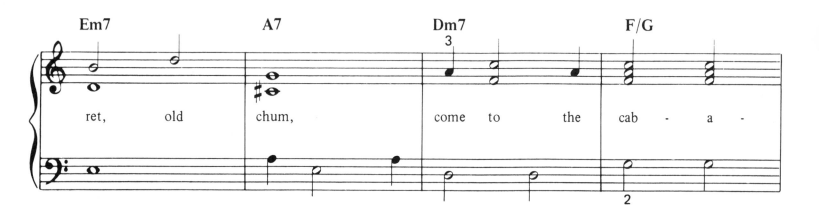

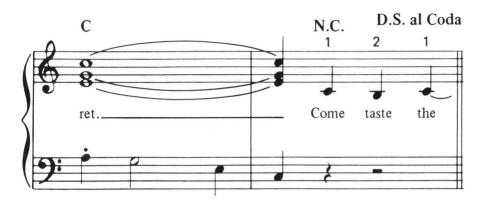

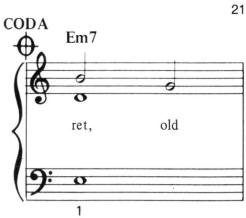

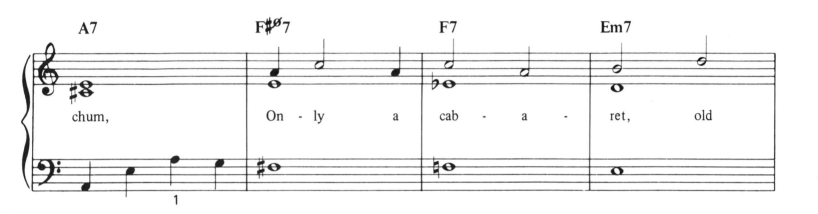

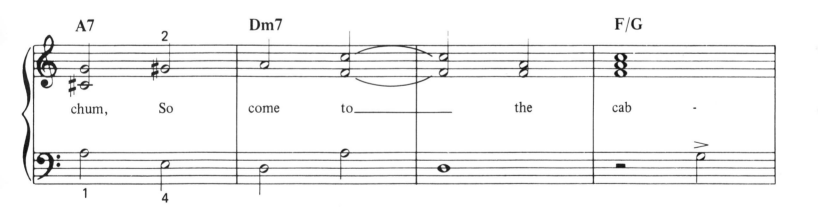

CAN YOU FEEL THE LOVE TONIGHT

Disney Presents THE LION KING: THE BROADWAY MUSICAL

Music by ELTON JOHN
Lyrics by TIM RICE

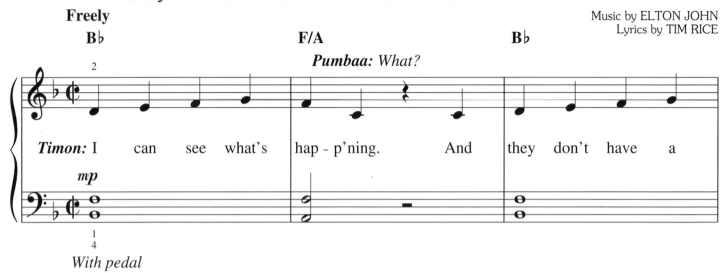

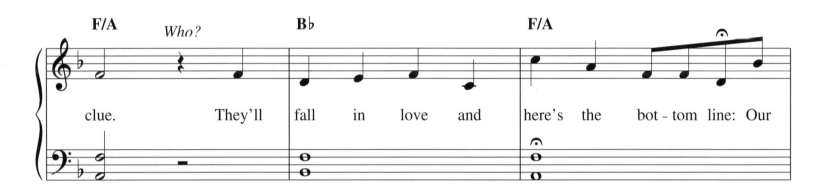

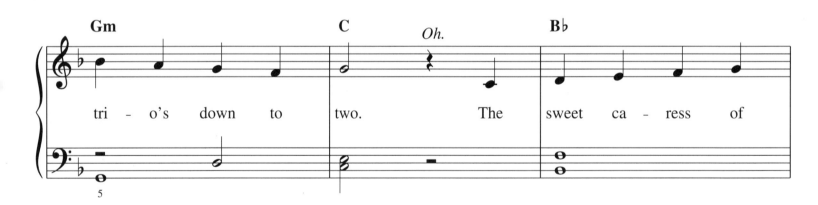

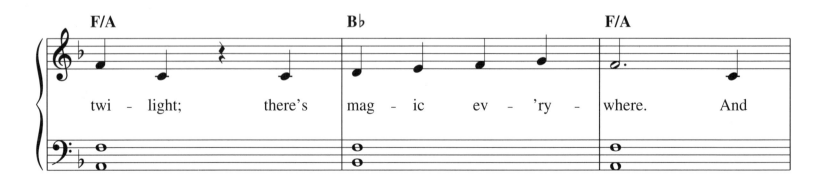

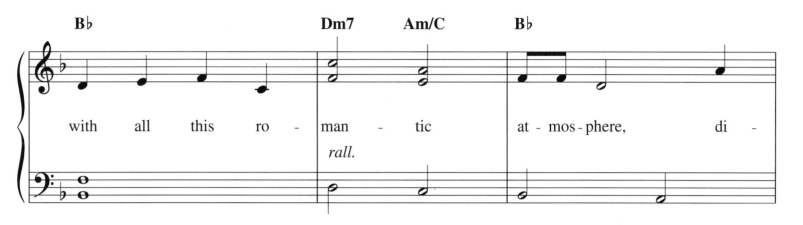

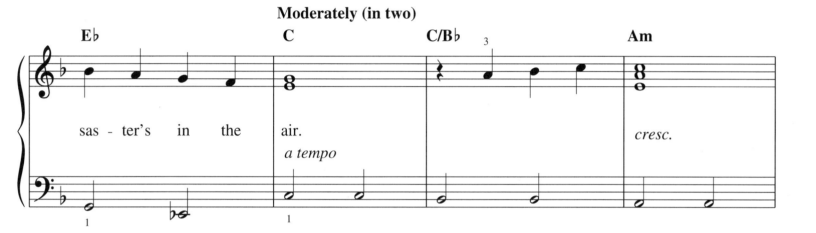

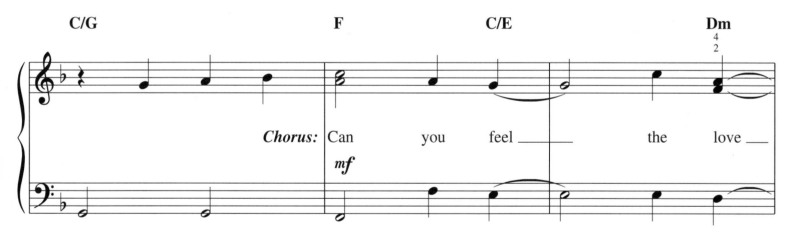

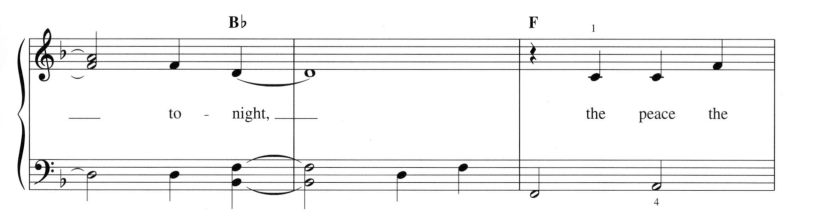

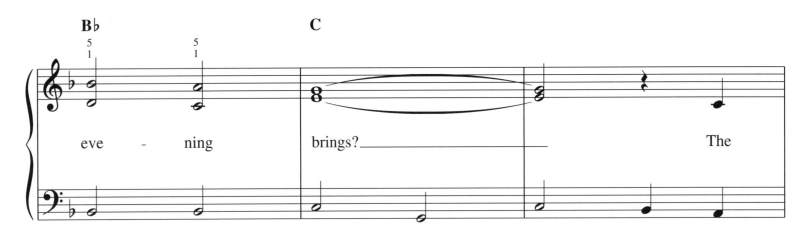

eve - ning brings?_____ The

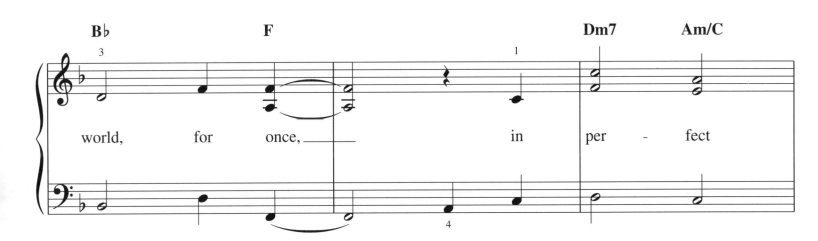

world, for once,_____ in per - fect

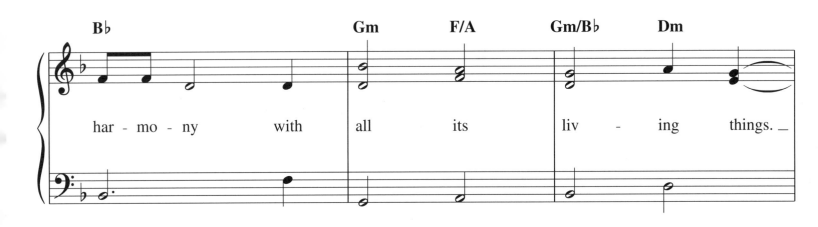

har - mo - ny with all its liv - ing things.__

dim.

Simba: So man - y things to

mp

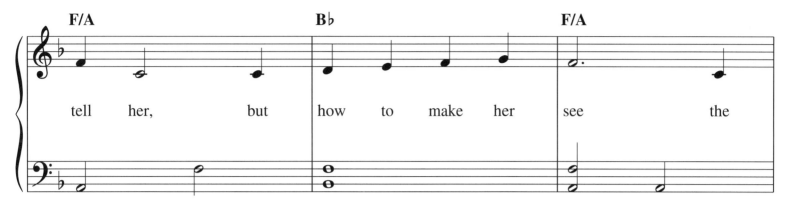

tell her, but how to make her see the

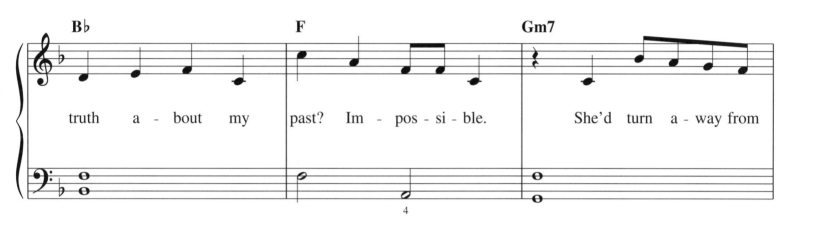

truth a - bout my past? Im - pos - si - ble. She'd turn a - way from

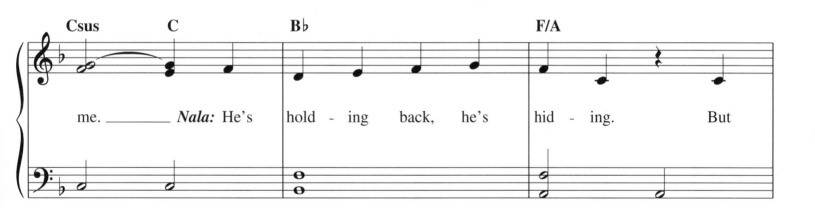

me. _____ *Nala:* He's hold - ing back, he's hid - ing. But

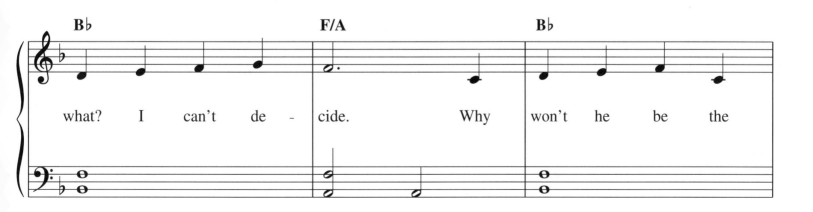

what? I can't de - cide. Why won't he be the

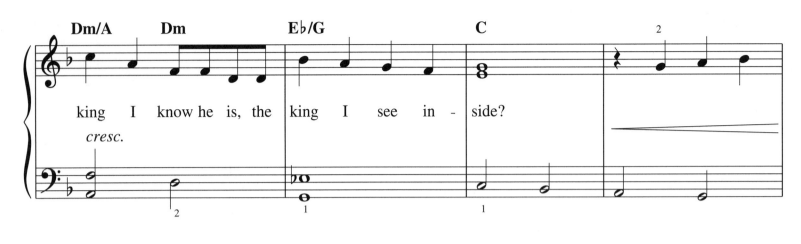

king I know he is, the king I see in - side?

Chorus: Can you feel ____ the love ____ to - night, ____

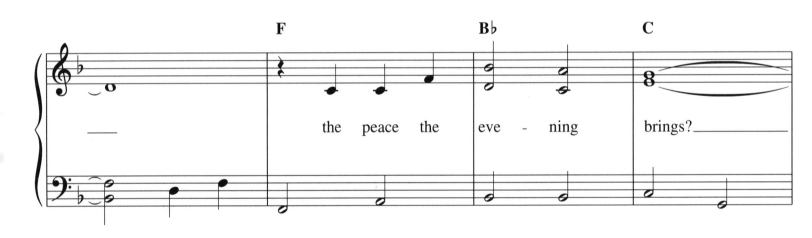

____ the peace the eve - ning brings? ____

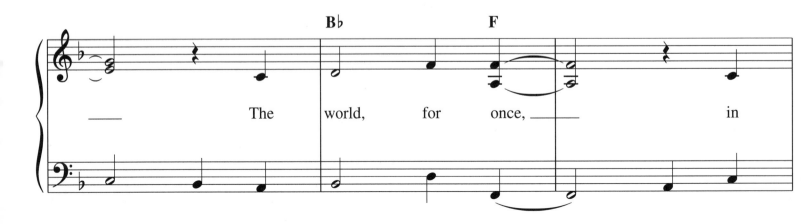

____ The world, for once, ____ in

per - fect har - mo - ny with all its

liv - ing things. Can you feel

the love to - night?

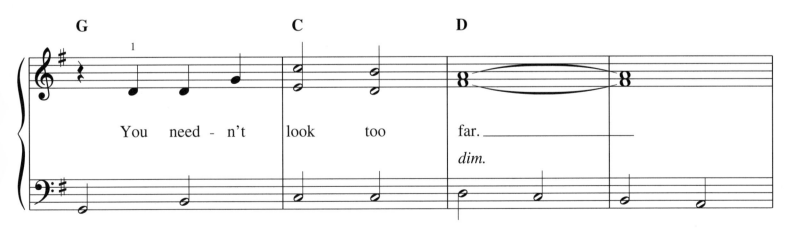

You need - n't look too far.

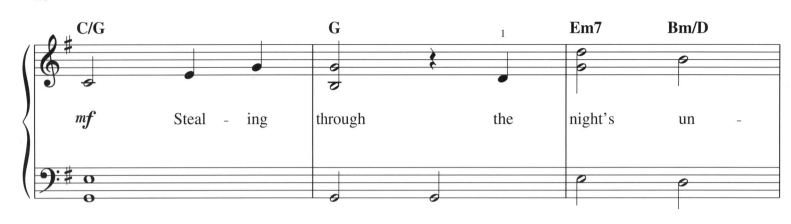

Steal - ing through the night's un -

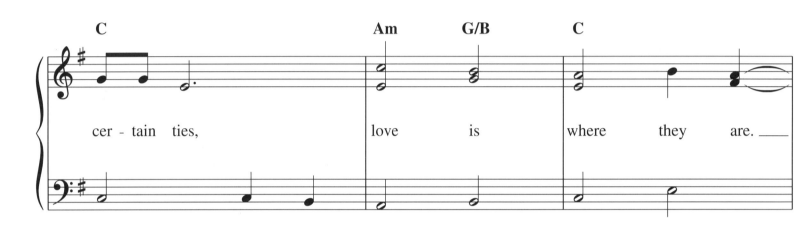

cer - tain - ties, love is where they are. ___

___ *Timon:* And if he

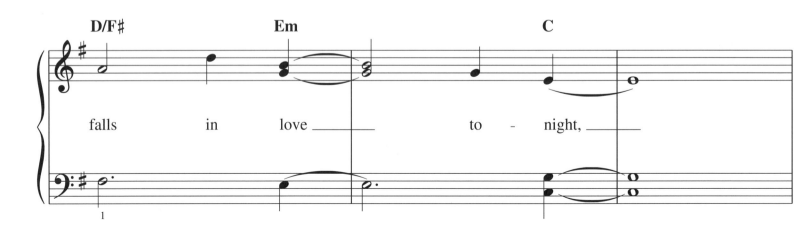

falls in love ___ to - night, ___

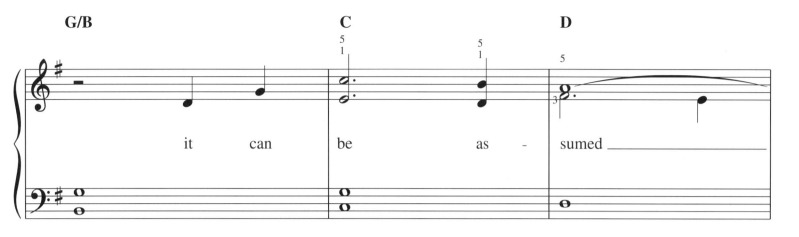

it can be as - sumed _____

_____ *Pumbaa:* his care - free days with

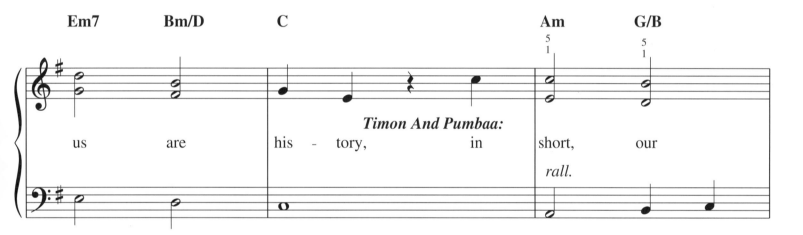

us are his - tory, in short, our

Timon And Pumbaa:

rall.

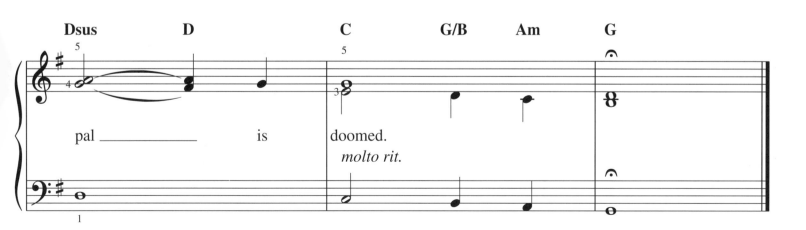

pal _____ is doomed.

molto rit.

DAY BY DAY
from the Musical GODSPELL

Words and Music by
STEPHEN SCHWARTZ

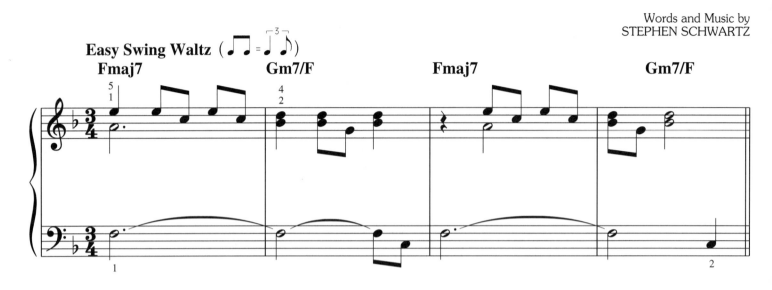

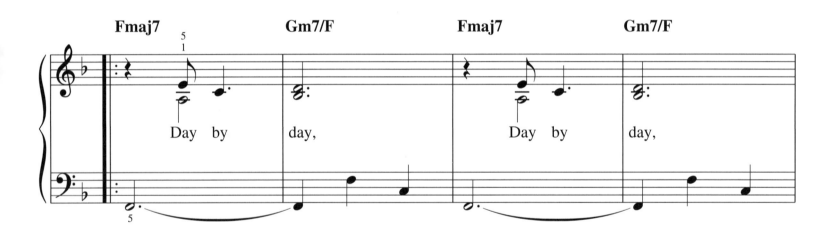

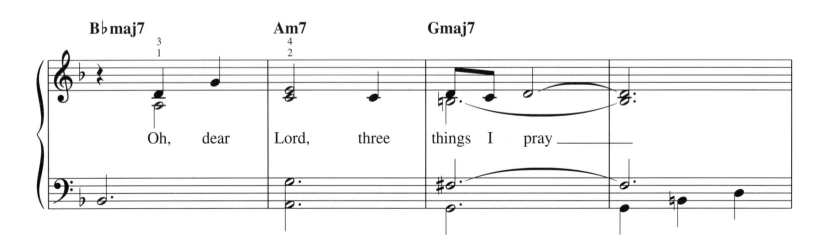

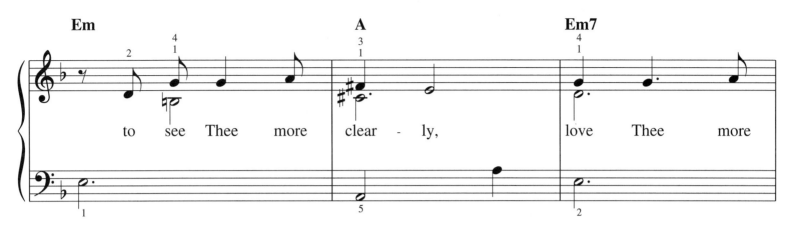

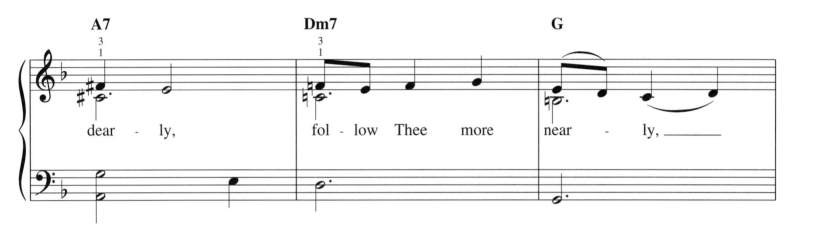

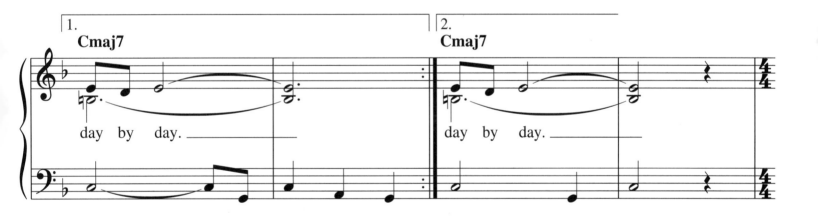

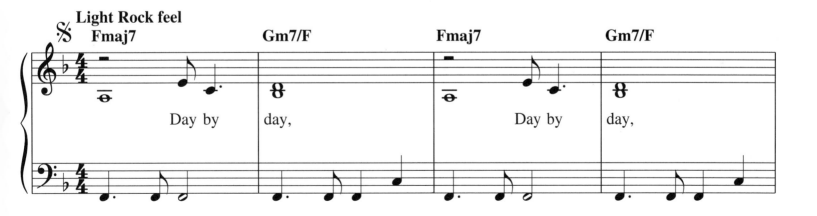

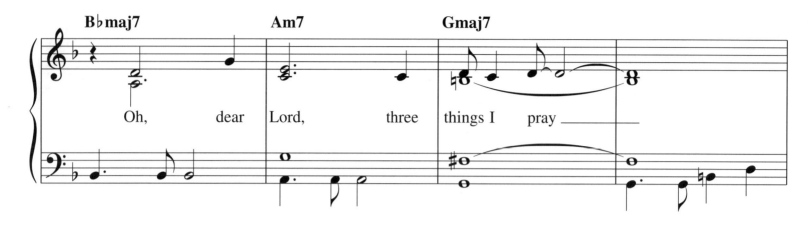

Oh, dear Lord, three things I pray

to see Thee more clear - ly, _____ love Thee more

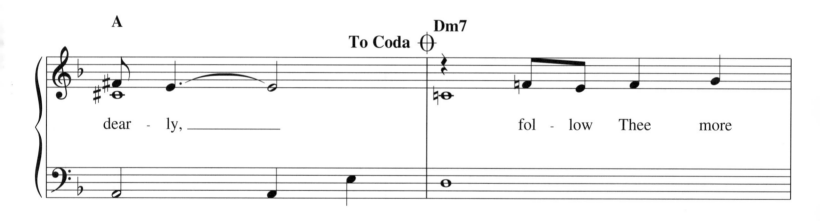

dear - ly, _____ fol - low Thee more

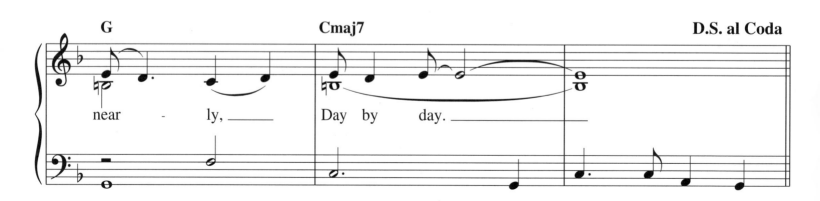

near - ly, _____ Day by day. _____

CODA

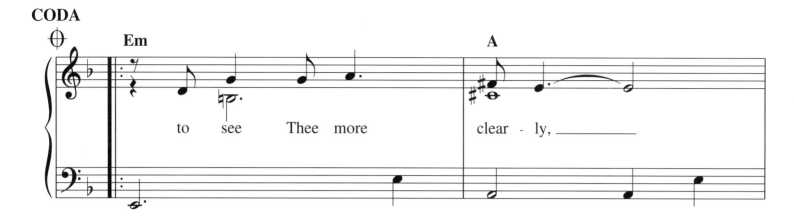

to see Thee more clear - ly, _____

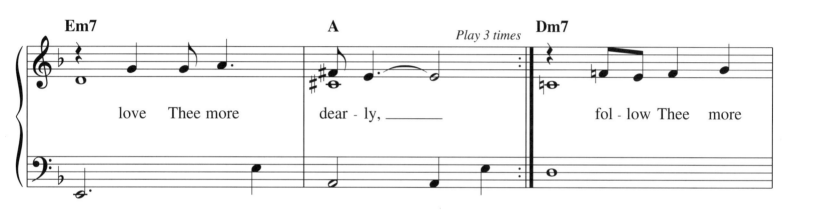

love Thee more dear - ly, _____ fol - low Thee more

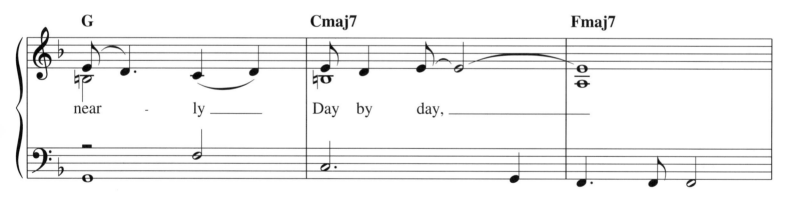

near - ly _____ Day by day, _____

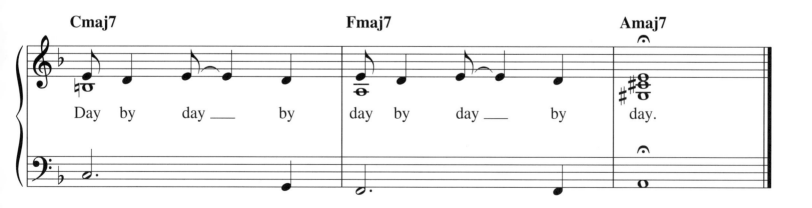

Day by day ___ by day by day ___ by day.

DON'T CRY FOR ME ARGENTINA

from EVITA

Words by TIM RICE
Music by ANDREW LLOYD WEBBER

Moderate Tango tempo

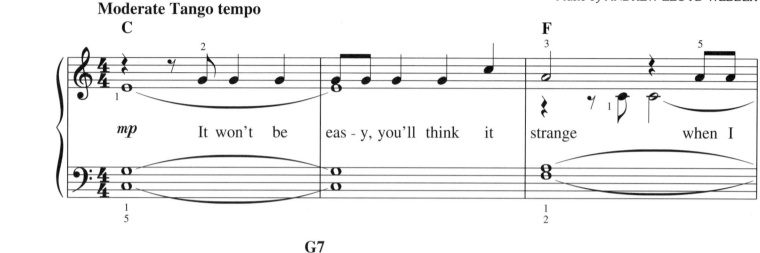

It won't be eas-y, you'll think it strange when I

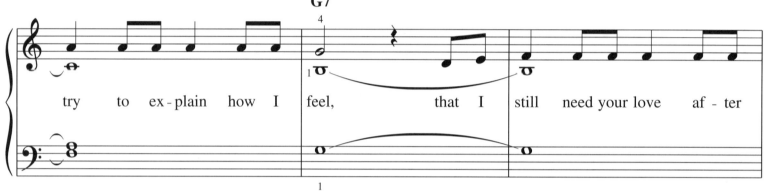

try to ex-plain how I feel, that I still need your love af-ter

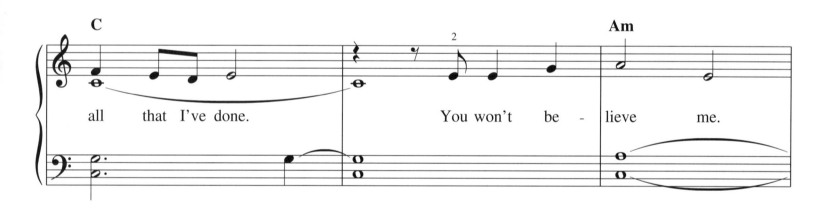

all that I've done. You won't be-lieve me.

All you will see is a girl you once knew, al-though she's dressed up to the

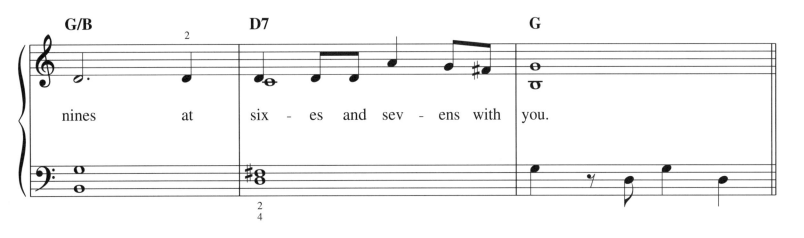

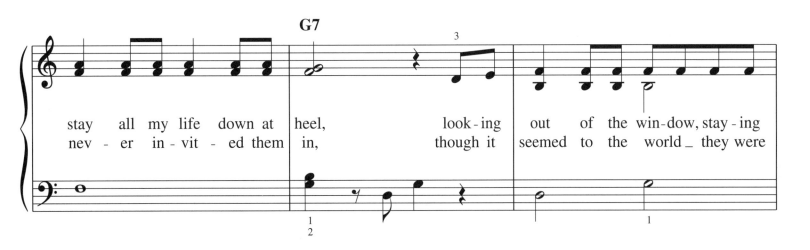

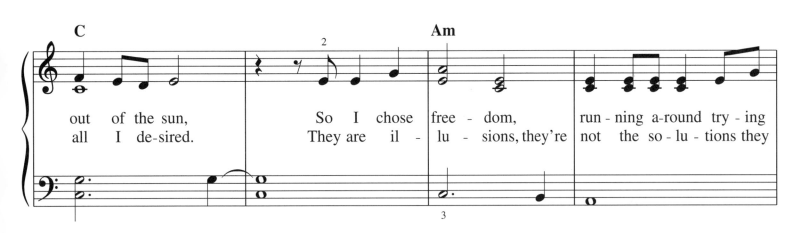

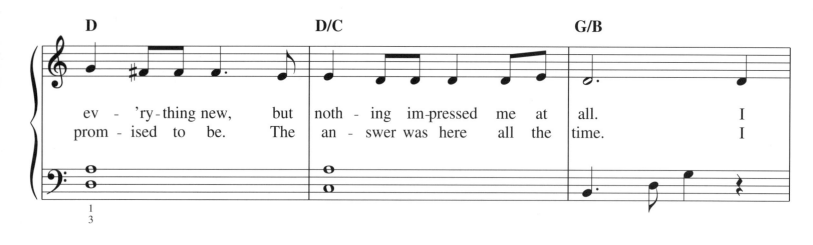

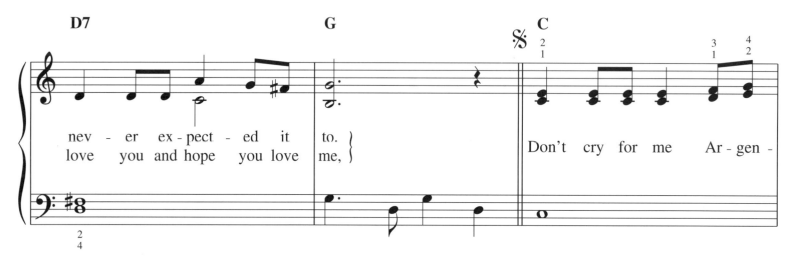

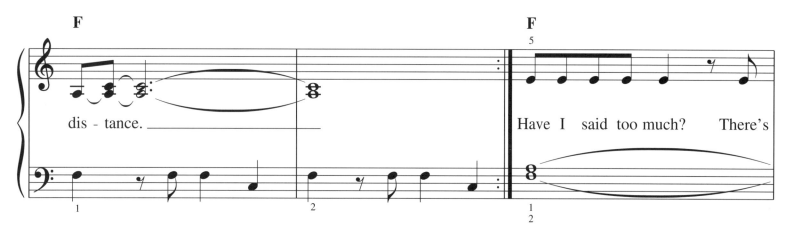

dis - tance. _____

Have I said too much? There's

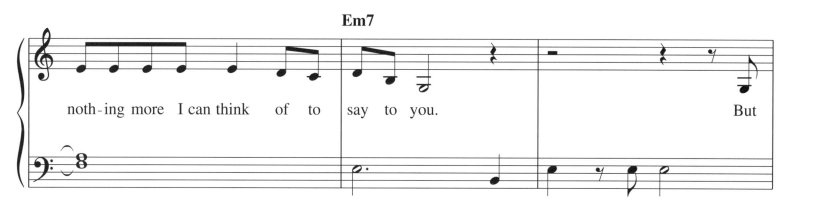

noth-ing more I can think of to say to you.

But

all you have to do is look at me to know that ev - 'ry word is true.

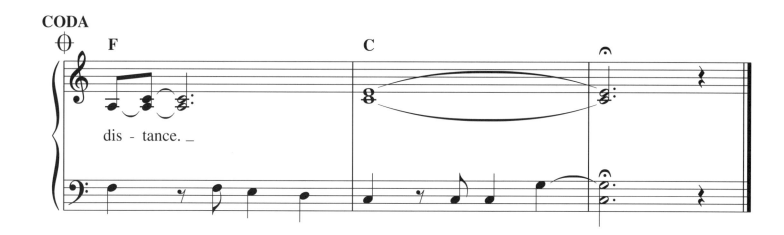

dis - tance. _

I DREAMED A DREAM

from LES MISÉRABLES

Music by CLAUDE-MICHEL SCHÖNBERG
Lyrics by HERBERT KRETZMER
Original Text by ALAIN BOUBLIL and JEAN-MARC NATEL

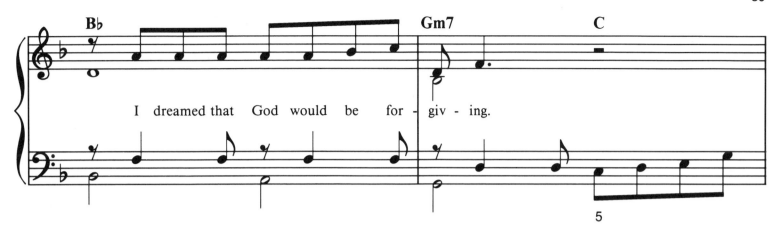

I dreamed that God would be for - giv - ing.

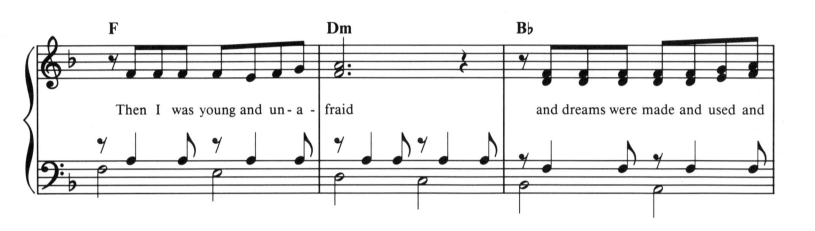

Then I was young and un - a - fraid and dreams were made and used and

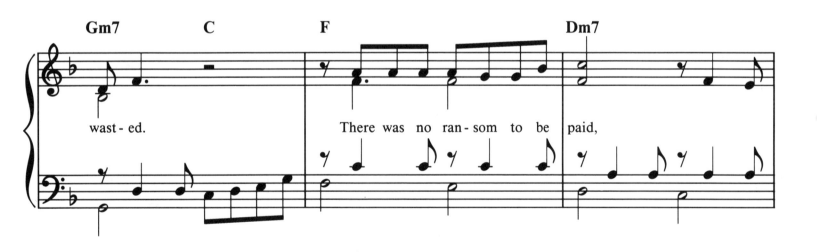

wast - ed. There was no ran - som to be paid,

no song un - sung no wine un - tast - ed. But the ti - gers come at

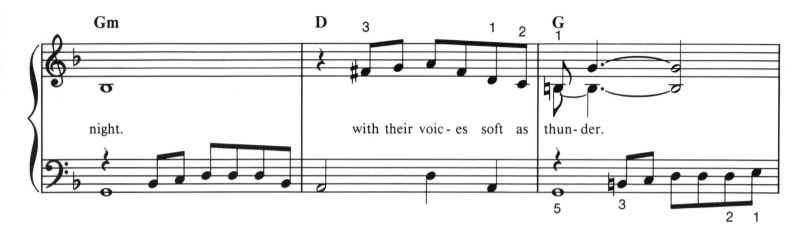

night.　with their voic- es　soft　as　thun- der.

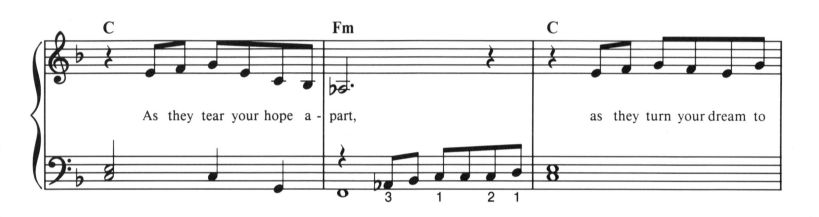

As　they　tear　your　hope　a - part,　　as　they　turn　your dream　to

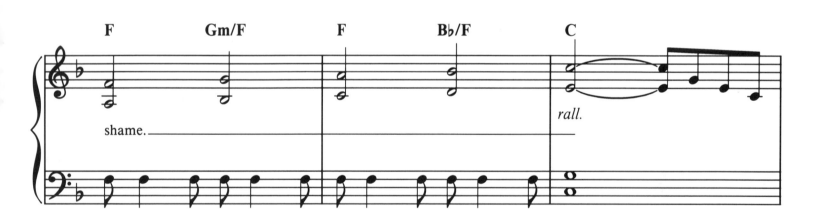

shame.＿＿＿＿＿＿＿＿＿＿＿＿＿＿＿
rall.

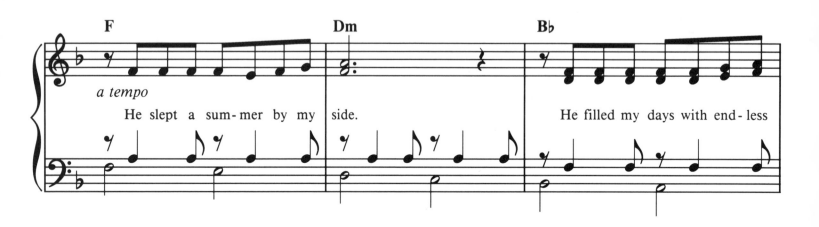

a tempo

He　slept　a　sum- mer　by　my　side.　　He　filled　my　days　with　end- less

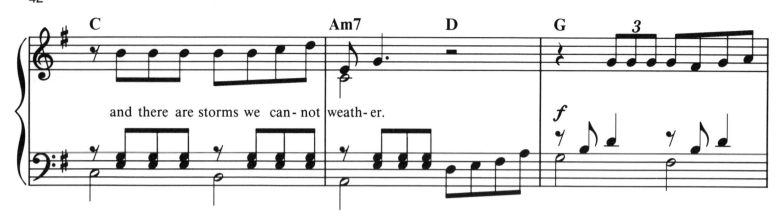

and there are storms we can-not weath-er.

I had a dream my life would be so dif-f'rent from this hell I'm

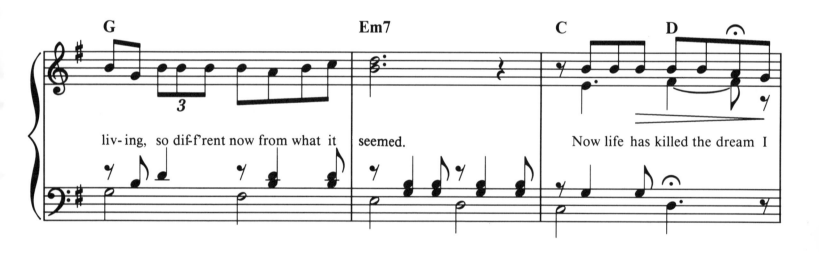

liv-ing, so dif-f'rent now from what it seemed. Now life has killed the dream I

dreamed.

I WHISTLE A HAPPY TUNE

from THE KING AND I

Lyrics by OSCAR HAMMERSTEIN II
Music by RICHARD RODGERS

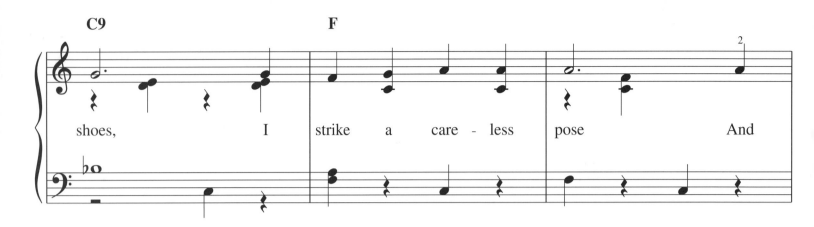

shoes, I strike a care - less pose And

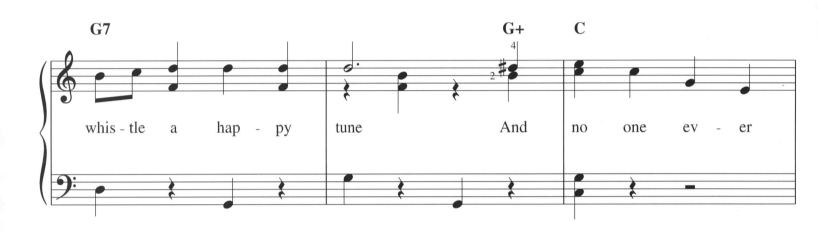

whis - tle a hap - py tune And no one ev - er

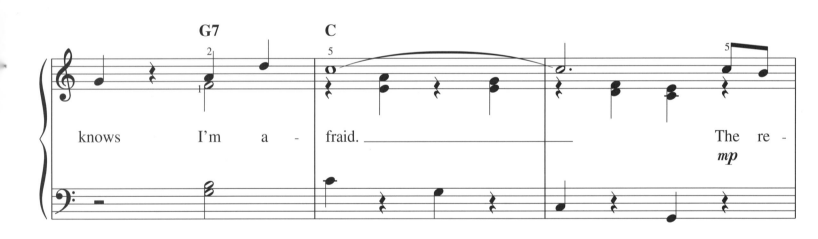

knows I'm a - fraid. _____ The re -

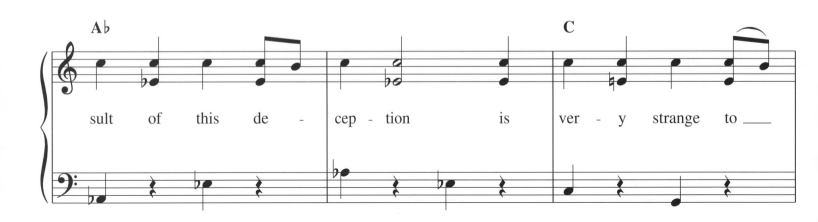

sult of this de - cep - tion is ver - y strange to ____

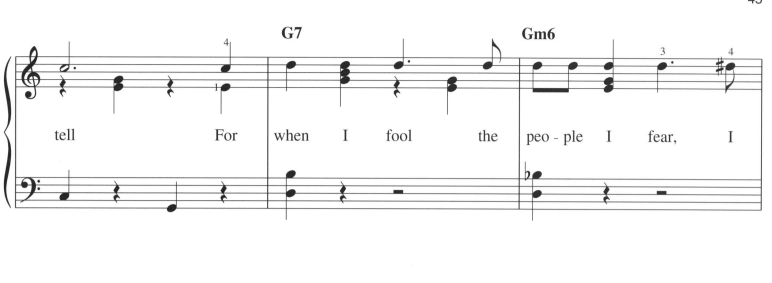

tell   For when I fool the peo - ple I fear, I

fool my - self as well!   I whis - tle a hap - py

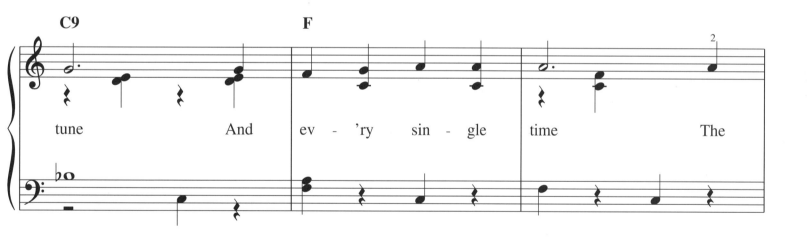

tune   And ev - 'ry sin - gle time   The

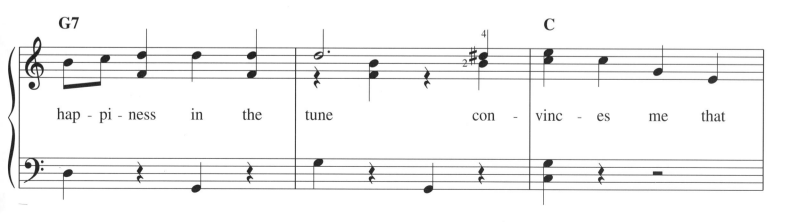

hap - pi - ness in the tune   con - vinc - es me that

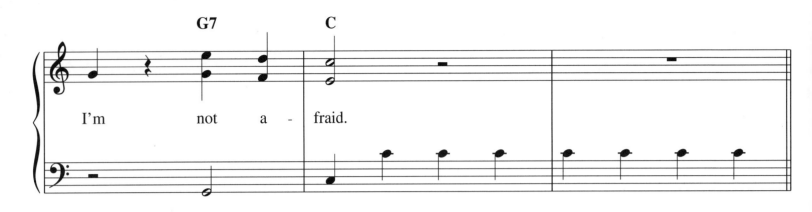

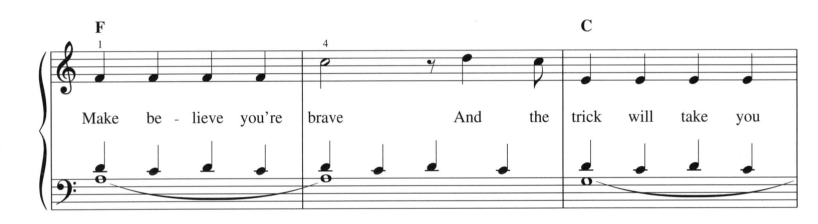

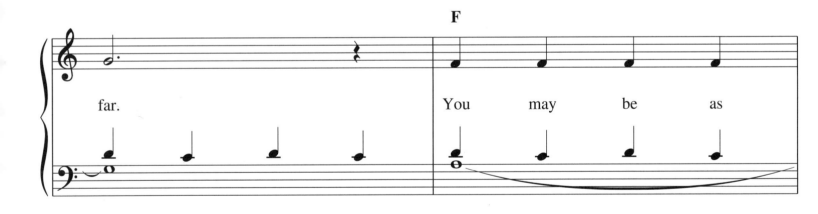

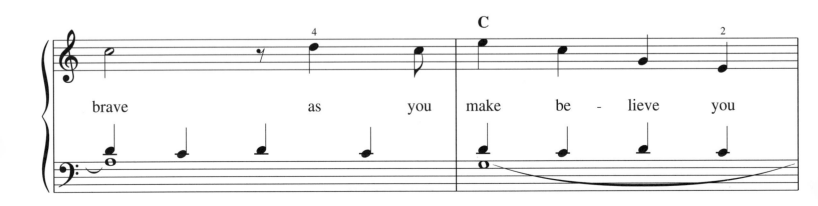

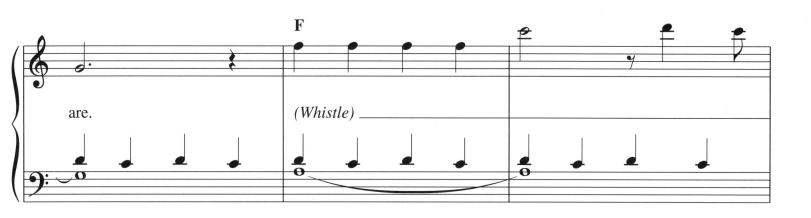

are. (Whistle)

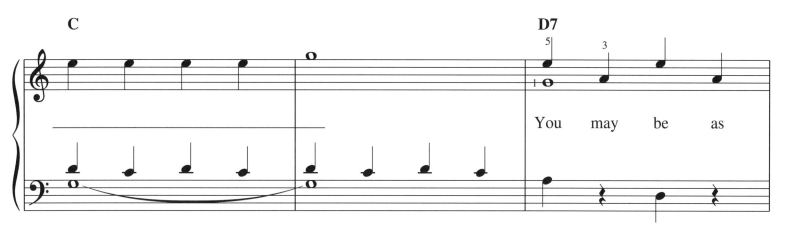

C | D7

You may be as

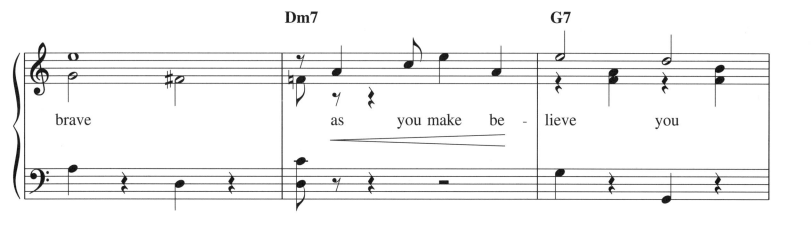

Dm7 | G7

brave | as you make be - lieve you

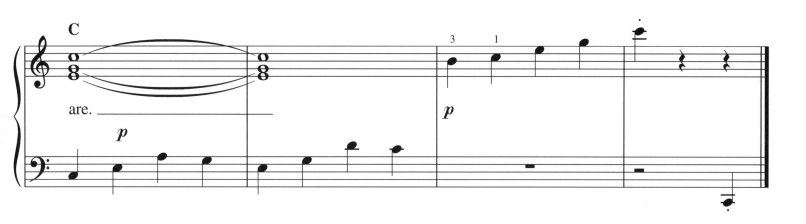

C

are. | *p*

IF I LOVED YOU

from CAROUSEL

Lyrics by OSCAR HAMMERSTEIN II
Music by RICHARD RODGERS

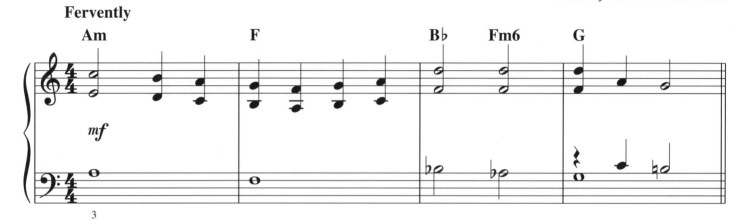

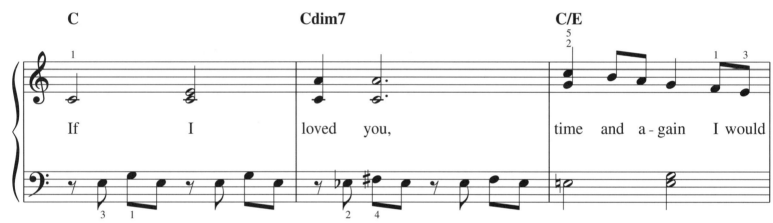

loved you / words would-n't come in an eas - y way.

'Round in cir - cles I'd go.

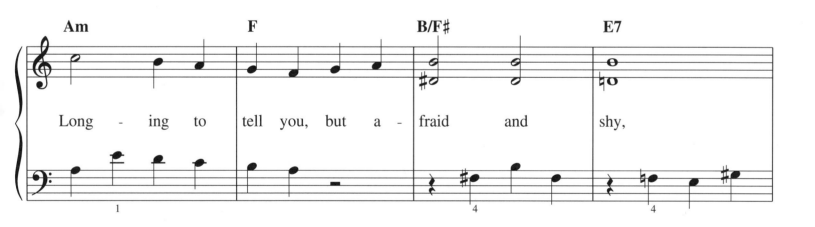

Long - ing to tell you, but a - fraid and shy,

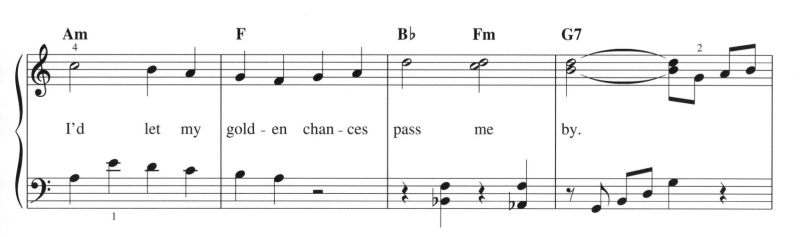

I'd let my gold - en chan - ces pass me by.

C   **Cdim7**   **C**

Soon   you'd   leave me.   Off   you would go   in the

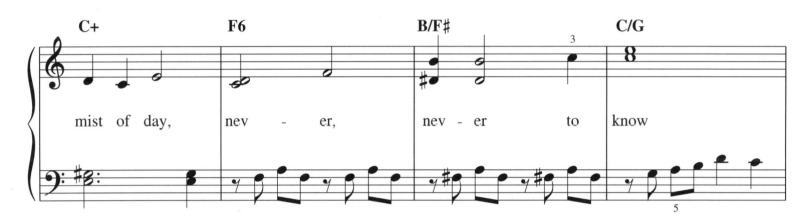

C+   **F6**   **B/F♯**   **C/G**

mist of day,   nev - er,   nev - er   to   know

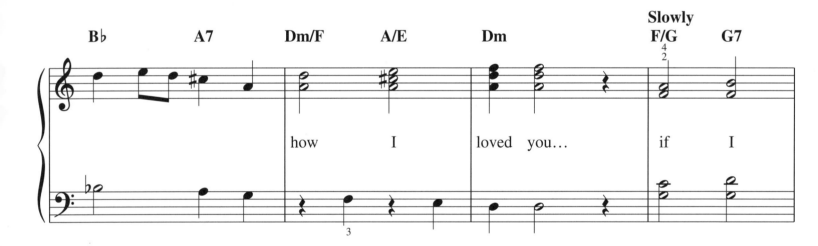

B♭   **A7**   **Dm/F**   **A/E**   **Dm**   **Slowly**   **F/G**   **G7**

how   I   loved   you…   if   I

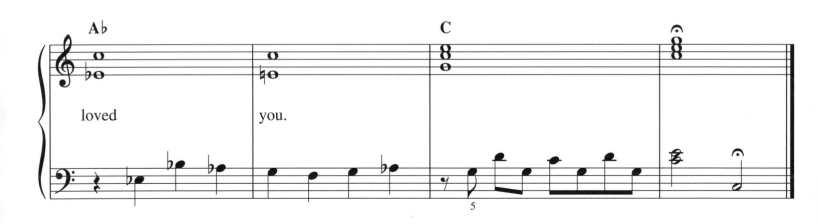

A♭   **C**

loved   you.

THE LAST NIGHT OF THE WORLD

from MISS SAIGON

Music by CLAUDE-MICHEL SCHÖNBERG
Lyrics by RICHARD MALTBY Jr. & ALAIN BOUBLIL
Adapted From Original French Lyrics by ALAIN BOUBLIL

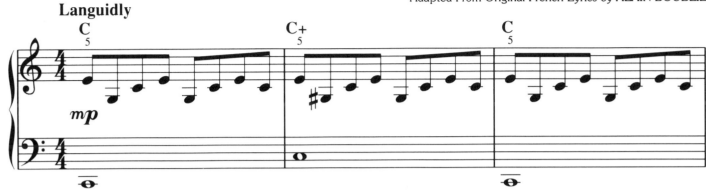

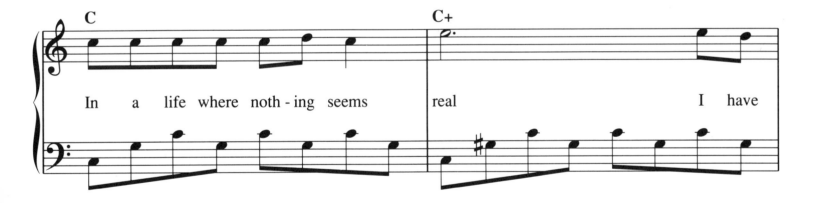

In a world that's mov-ing too fast.

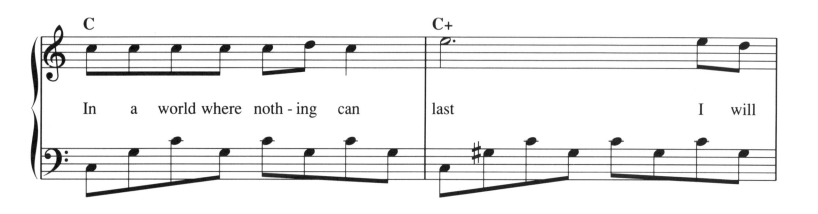

In a world where noth-ing can last I will

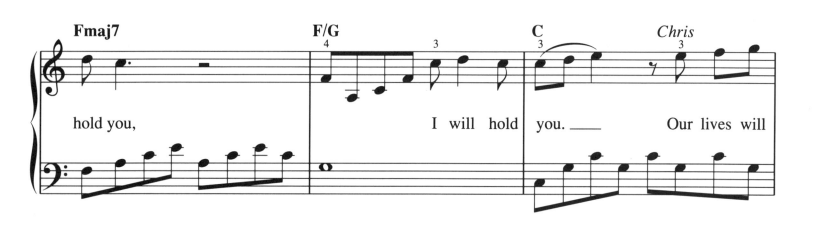

hold you, I will hold you. ____ Our lives will

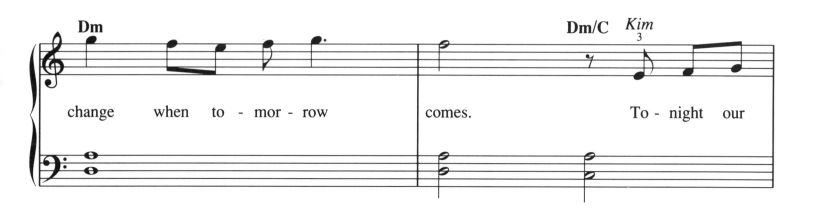

change when to-mor-row comes. To-night our

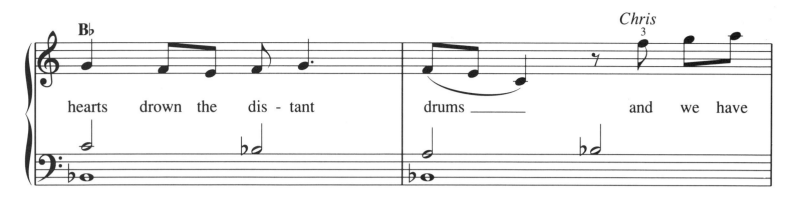

hearts drown the dis - tant drums _____ and we have

mu - sic al - right tear - ing the night. A song

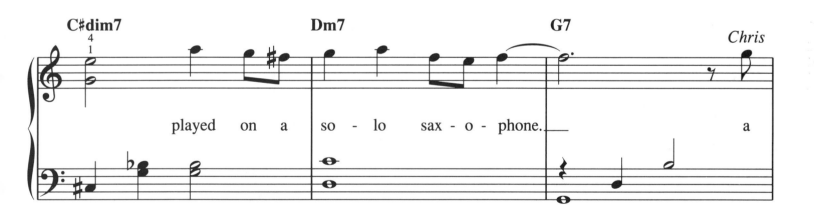

played on a so - lo sax - o - phone. a

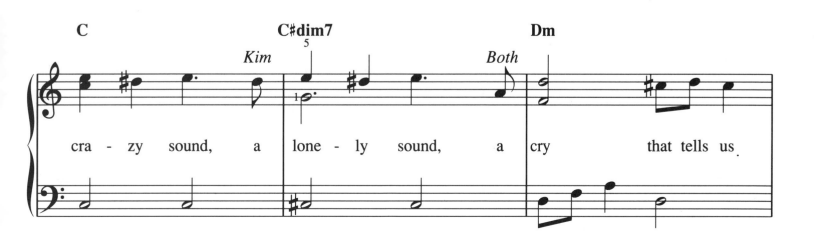

cra - zy sound, a lone - ly sound, a cry that tells us

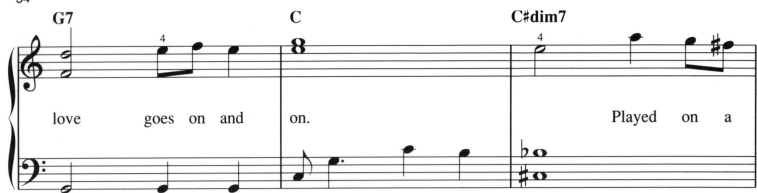

love goes on and on. Played on a

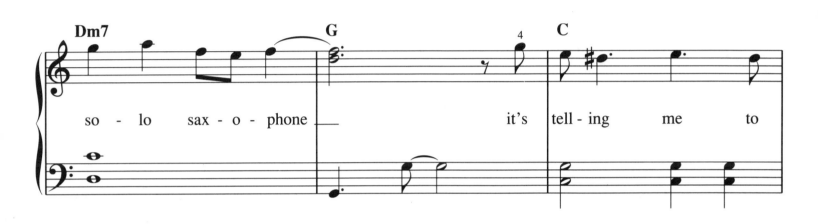

so - lo sax - o - phone it's tell - ing me to

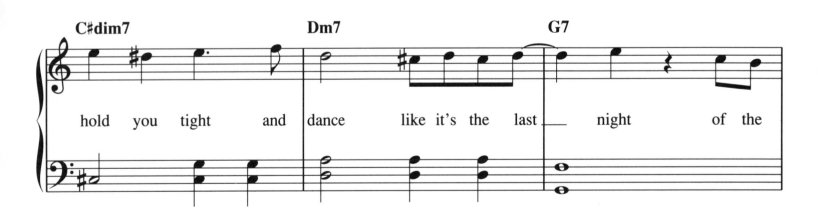

hold you tight and dance like it's the last night of the

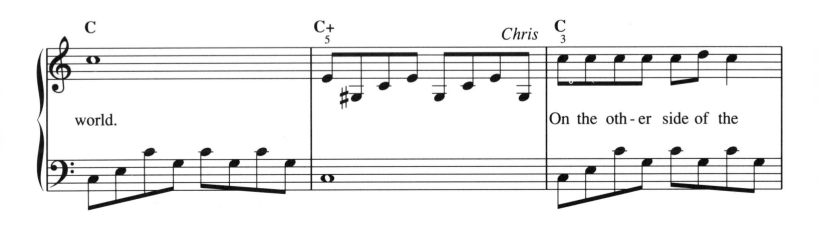

world. On the oth - er side of the

earth — there's a place where life still has worth. I will

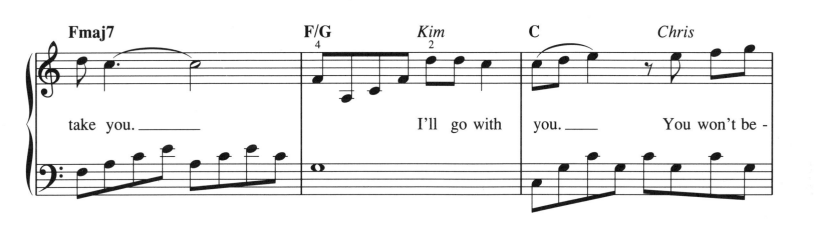

take you. — *Kim* I'll go with *Chris* you. — You won't be-

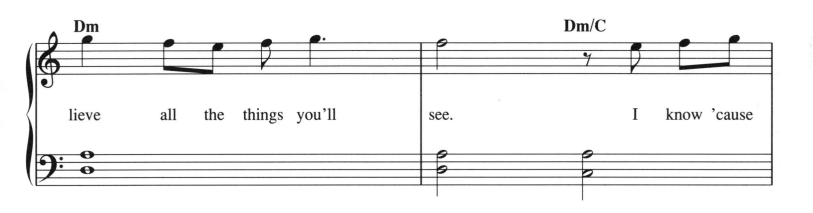

lieve all the things you'll see. I know 'cause

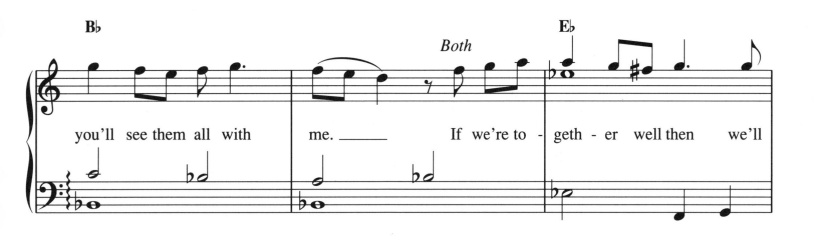

you'll see them all with me. — *Both* If we're to-geth-er well then we'll

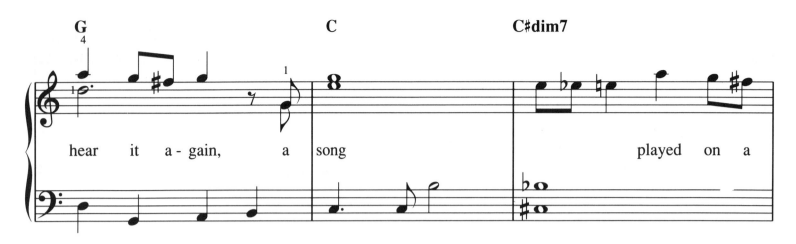

hear it a - gain, a song played on a

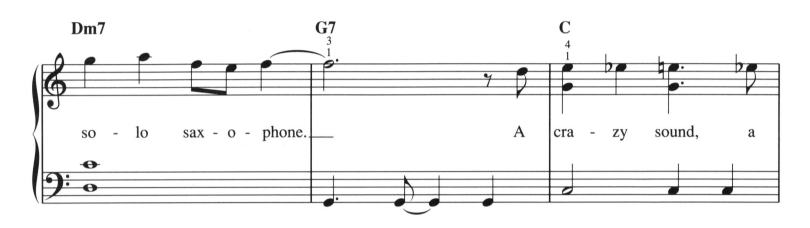

so - lo sax - o - phone. A cra - zy sound, a

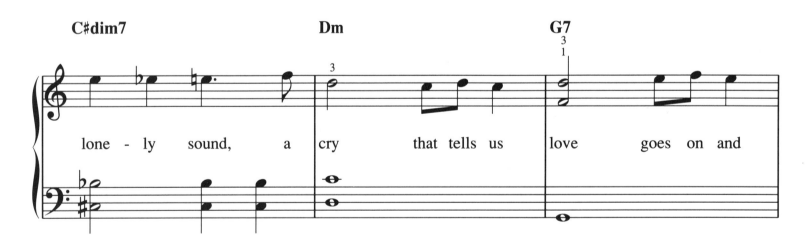

lone - ly sound, a cry that tells us love goes on and

on. Played on a so - lo sax - o - phone.

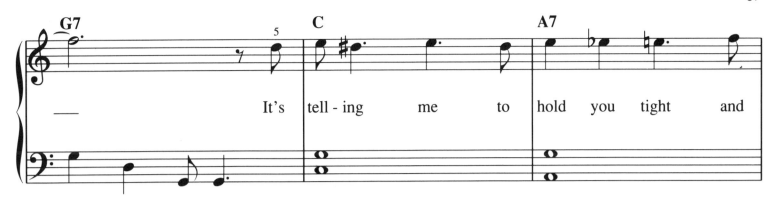

It's tell-ing me to hold you tight and

dance like it's the last night of the world.

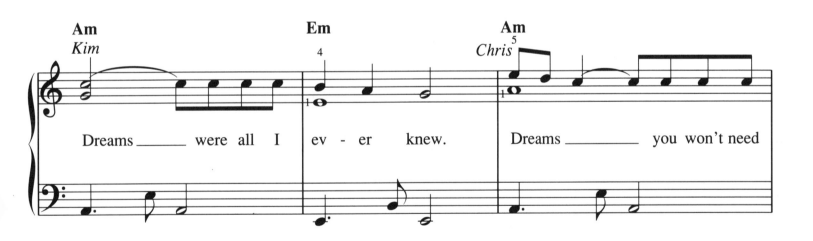

Dreams _____ were all I ev - er knew. Dreams _____ you won't need

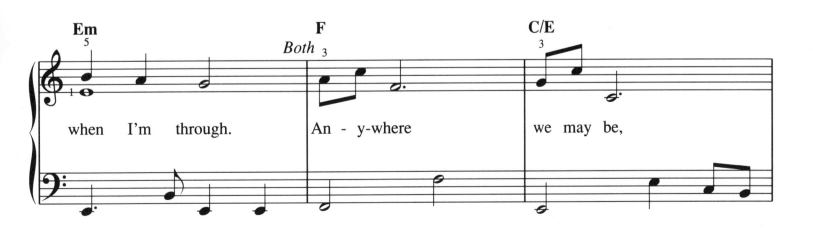

when I'm through. An - y-where we may be,

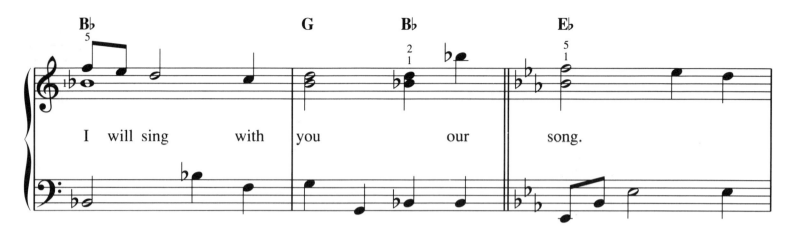

I will sing with you our song.

So

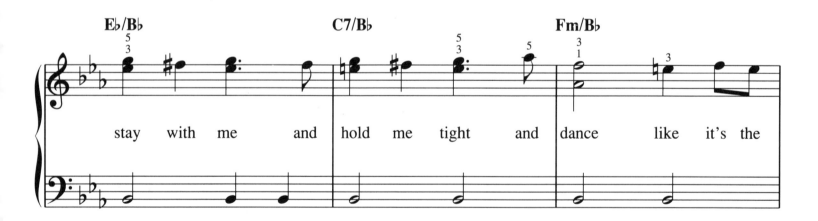

stay with me and hold me tight and dance like it's the

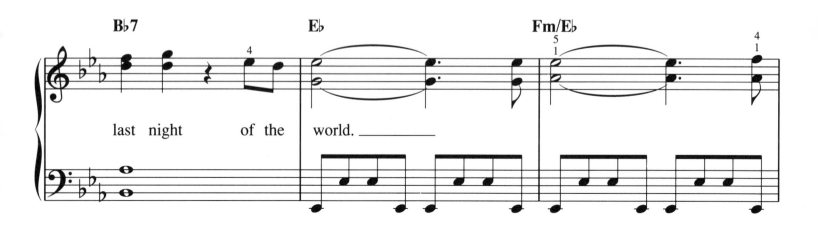

last night of the world.

LUCK BE A LADY
from GUYS AND DOLLS

By FRANK LOESSER

Moderately fast

Luck   be a   la - dy to - night.

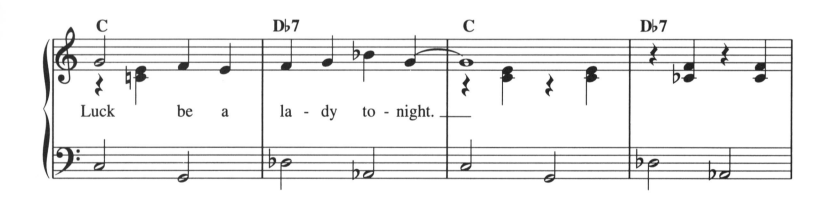

Luck   be a   la - dy to - night.

Luck   if you've   ev - er been a   la - dy to be -

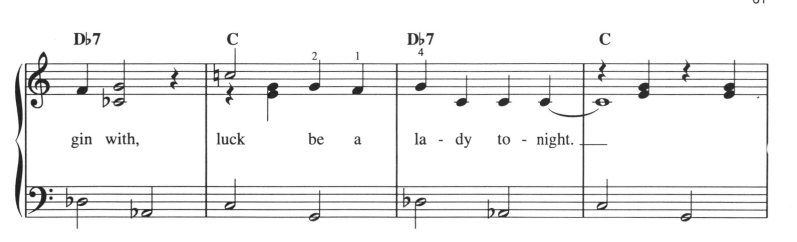

gin with, luck be a la - dy to - night.

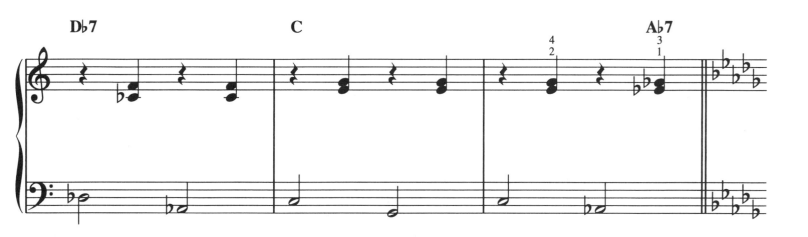

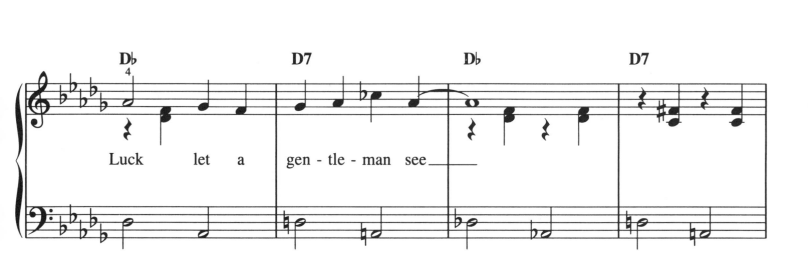

Luck let a gen - tle - man see____

how nice a dame you can be.____

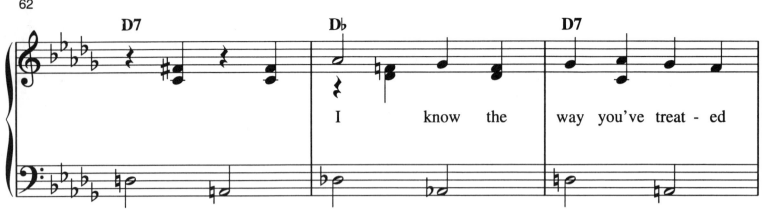

I know the way you've treat - ed

oth - er guys you've been with, luck be a

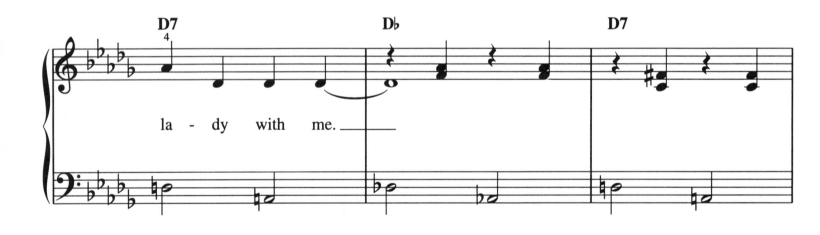

la - dy with me.

A la - dy does - n't

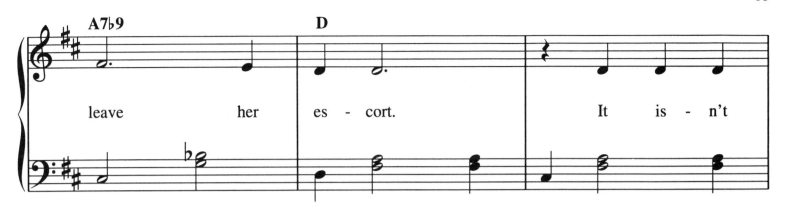

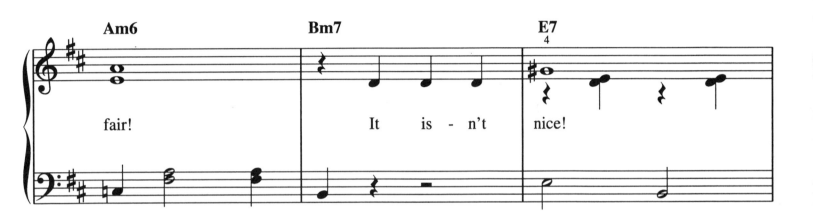

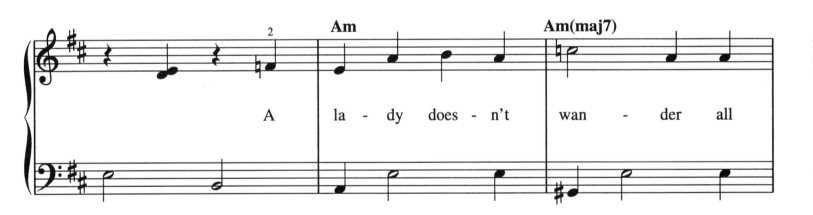

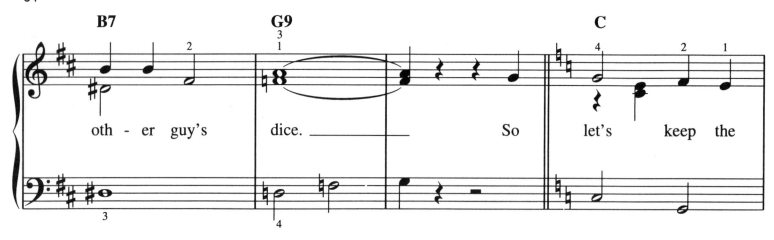

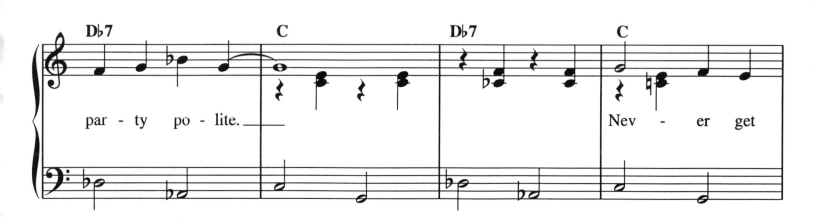

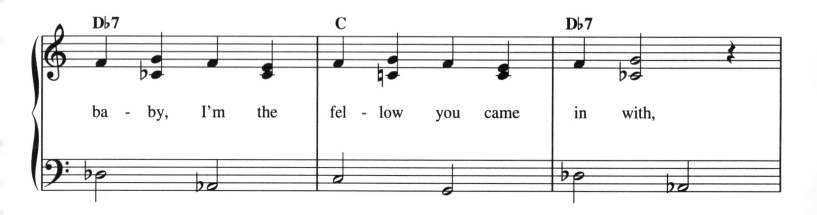

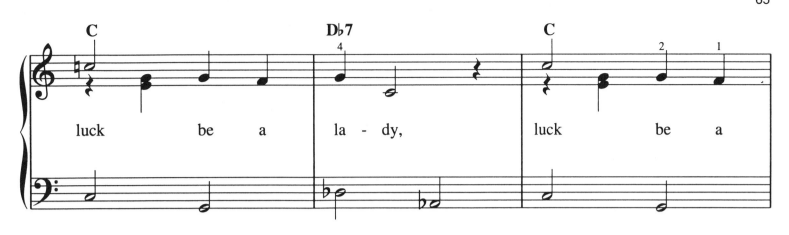

luck be a la - dy, luck be a

la - dy, luck be a la - dy to - night.

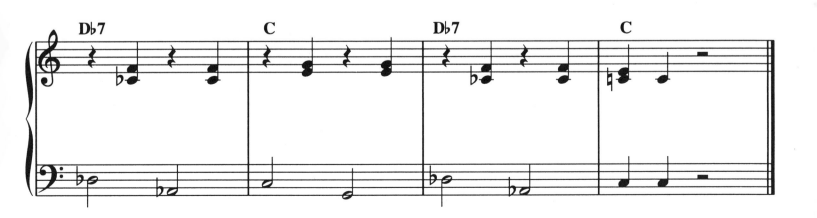

THE MUSIC OF THE NIGHT
from THE PHANTOM OF THE OPERA

Music by ANDREW LLOYD WEBBER
Lyrics by CHARLES HART
Additional Lyrics by RICHARD STILGOE

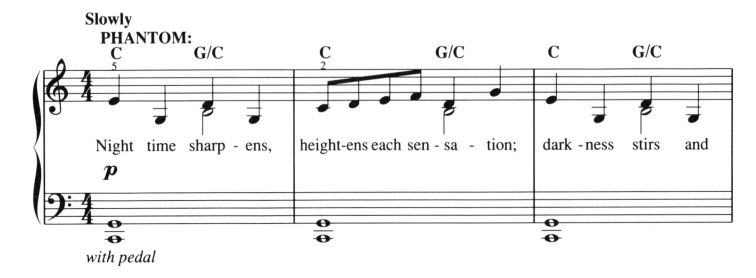

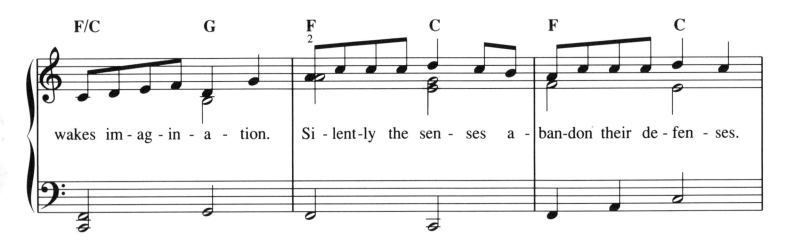

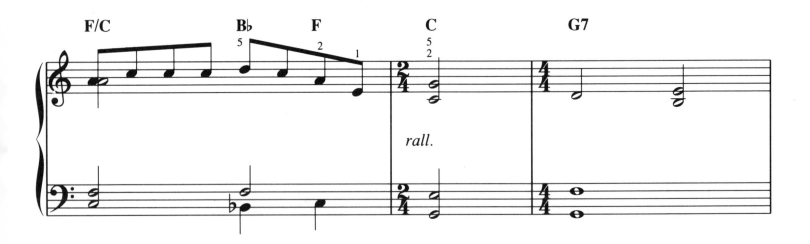

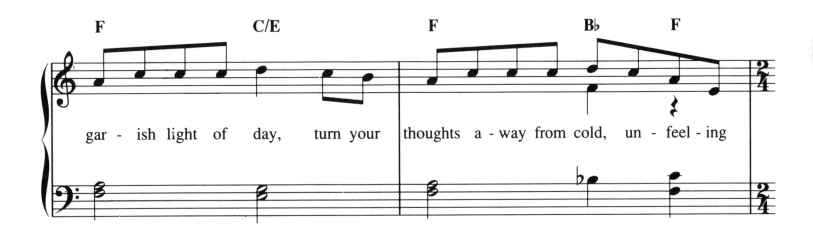

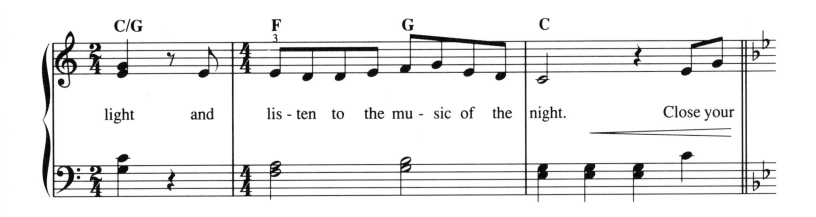

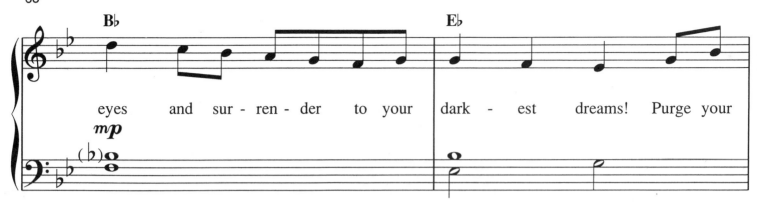

eyes and sur - ren - der to your dark - est dreams! Purge your

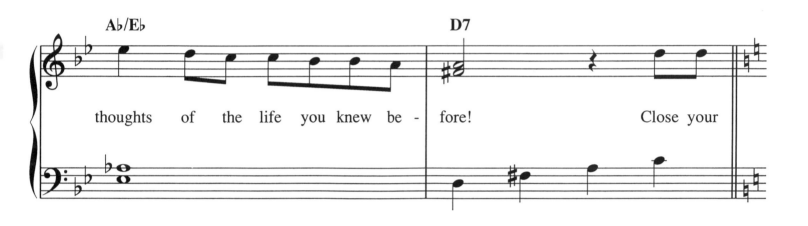

thoughts of the life you knew be - fore! Close your

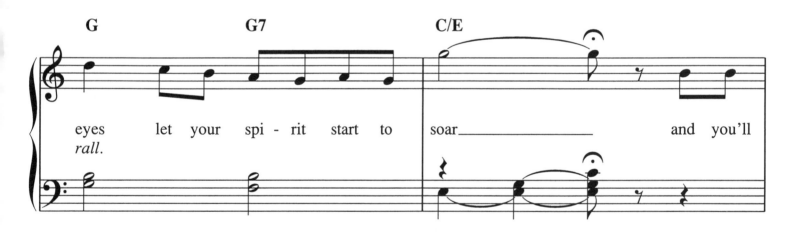

eyes let your spi - rit start to soar_____ and you'll

rall.

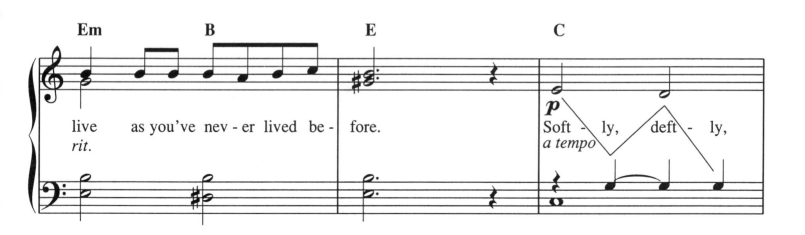

live as you've nev - er lived be - fore.

rit.

Soft - ly, deft - ly,

a tempo

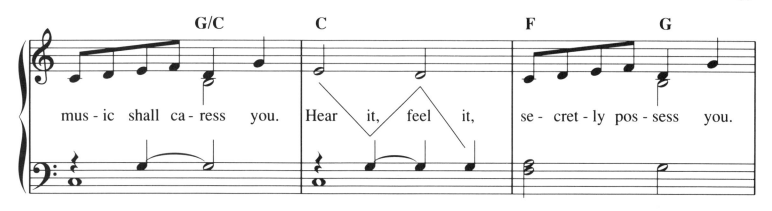

mus - ic shall ca - ress you. Hear it, feel it, se - cret - ly pos - sess you.

O - pen up your mind, let your fan - ta - sies un - wind in this

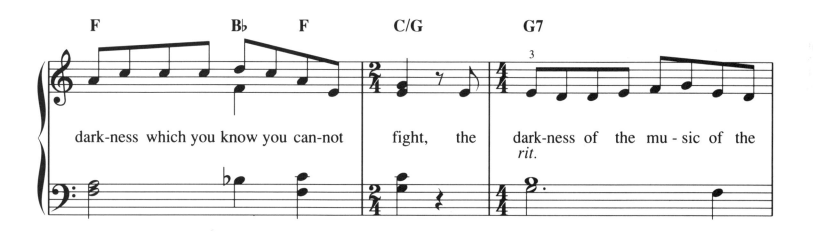

dark-ness which you know you can-not fight, the dark-ness of the mu - sic of the

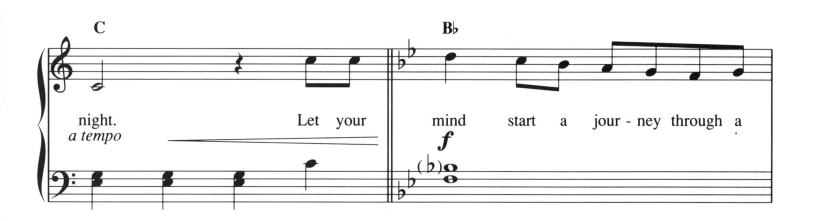

night. Let your mind start a jour - ney through a

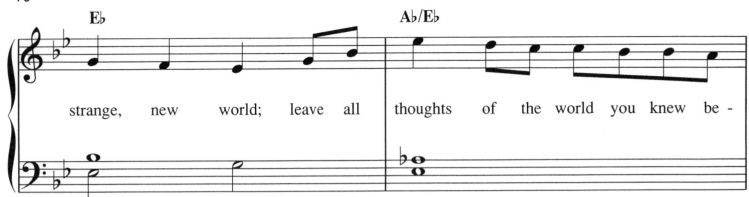

strange, new world; leave all thoughts of the world you knew be-

fore. Let your soul take you where you long to

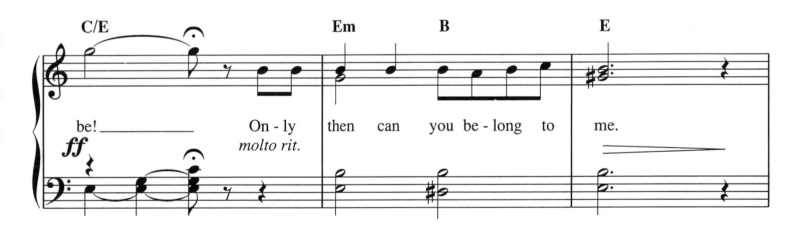

be! _____ On-ly then can you be-long to me.

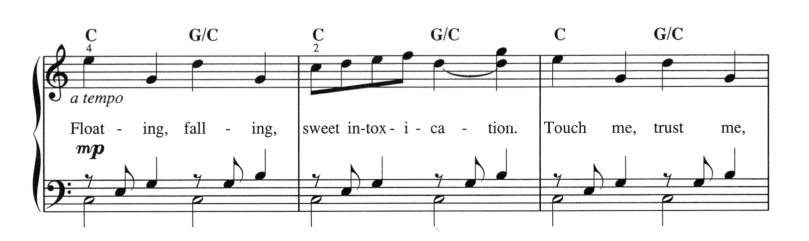

Float-ing, fall-ing, sweet in-tox-i-ca-tion. Touch me, trust me,

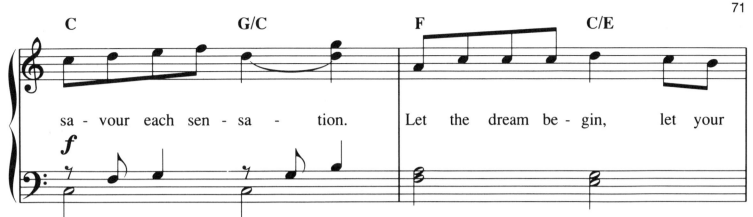

sa - vour each sen - sa - tion. Let the dream be - gin, let your

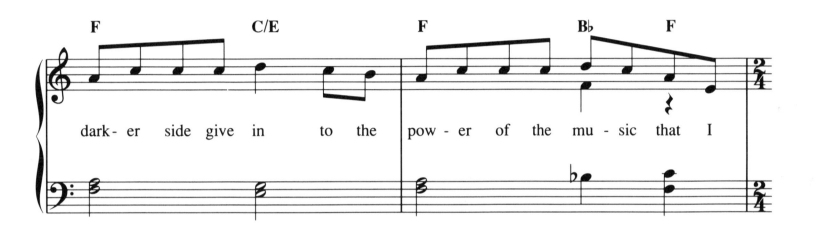

dark - er side give in to the pow - er of the mu - sic that I

write, the pow - er of the mu - sic of the night.

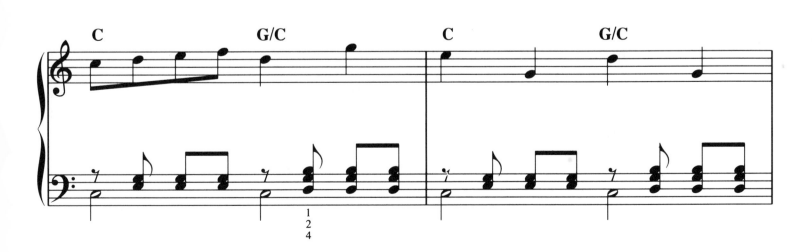

sa - vour each sen - sa - tion.

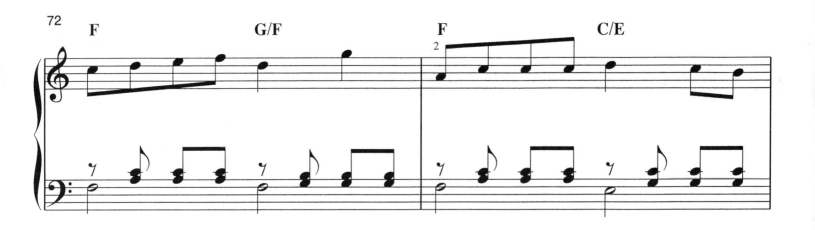

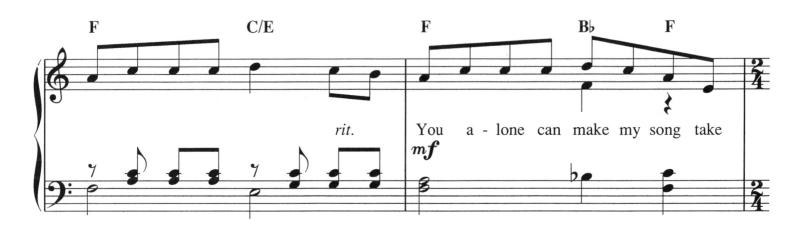

rit.

You a - lone can make my song take

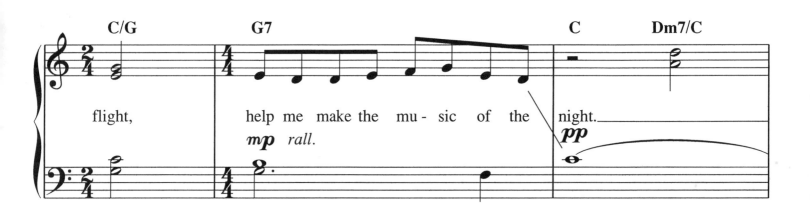

flight, help me make the mu - sic of the night.

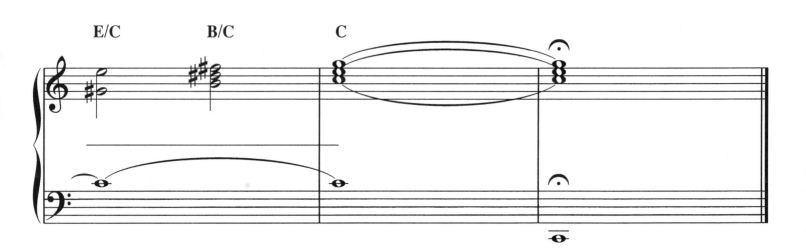

ON MY OWN

from LES MISÉRABLES

Music by CLAUDE-MICHEL SCHÖNBERG
Lyrics by ALAIN BOUBLIL, HERBERT KRETZMER, JOHN CAIRD,
TREVOR NUNN and JEAN-MARC NATEL

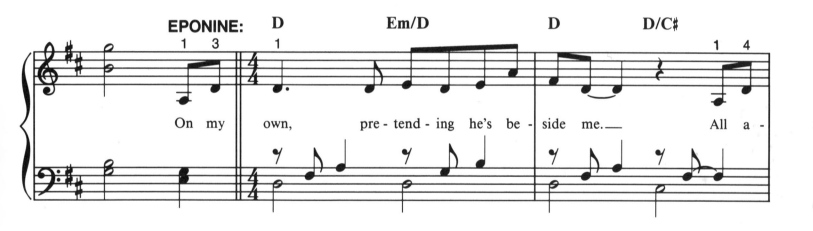

round me. And when I lose my way I close my eyes and he has

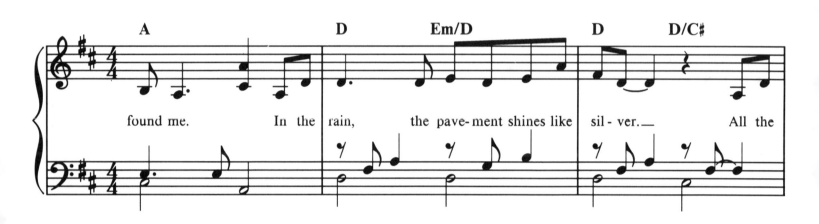

found me. In the rain, the pave-ment shines like sil-ver.___ All the

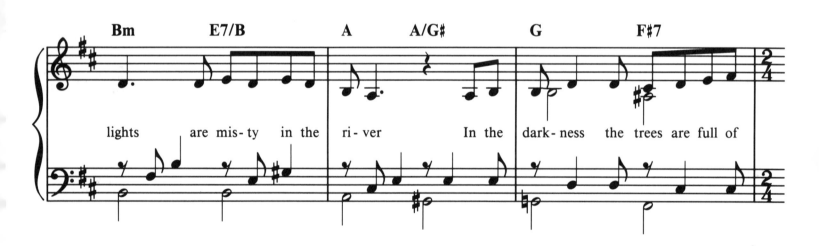

lights are mis-ty in the ri-ver In the dark-ness the trees are full of

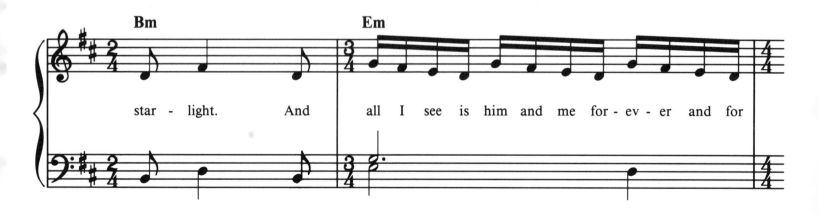

star-light. And all I see is him and me for-ev-er and for

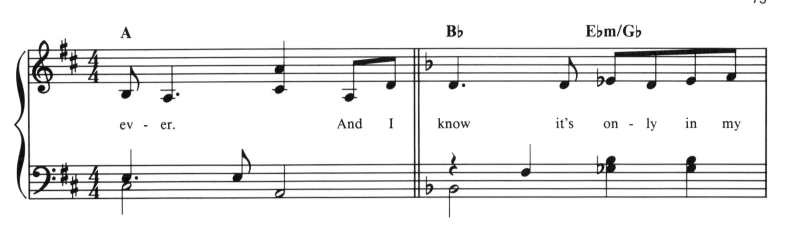

ev - er. And I know it's on - ly in my

mind that I'm talk - ing to my - self and not to him. And al -

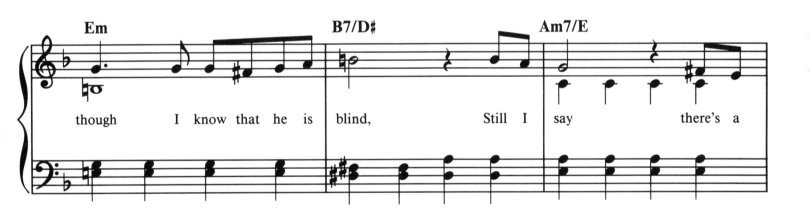

though I know that he is blind, Still I say there's a

way for us. I love him, but when the night is

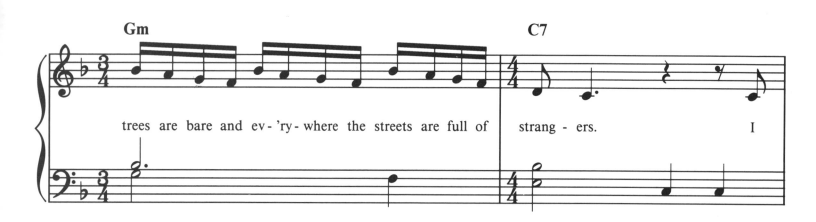

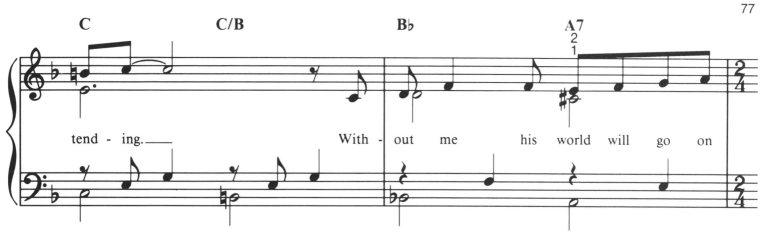

tend - ing.___ With - out me his world will go on

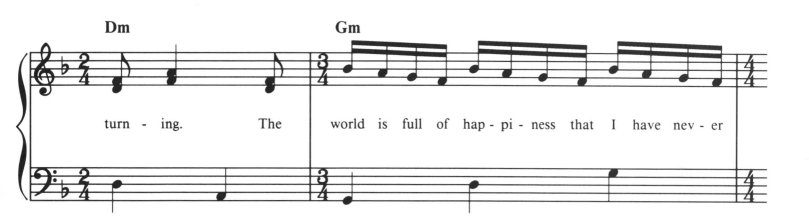

turn - ing. The world is full of hap - pi - ness that I have nev - er

known. I love him, I love him, I

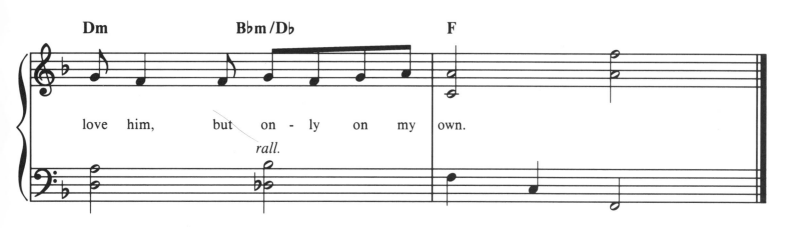

love him, but on - ly on my own.

rall.

MY FAVORITE THINGS

from THE SOUND OF MUSIC

Lyrics by OSCAR HAMMERSTEIN II
Music by RICHARD RODGERS

Lively, in one (♩. = 1 beat)

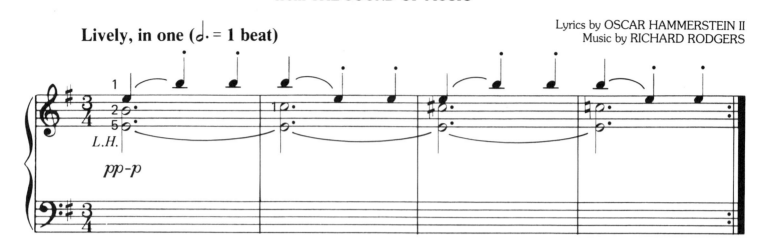

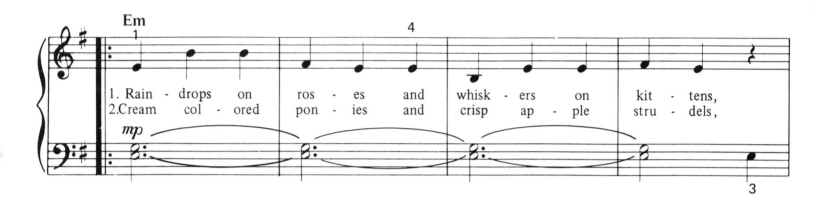

1. Rain - drops on ros - es and whisk - ers on kit - tens,
2. Cream col - ored pon - ies and crisp ap - ple stru - dels,

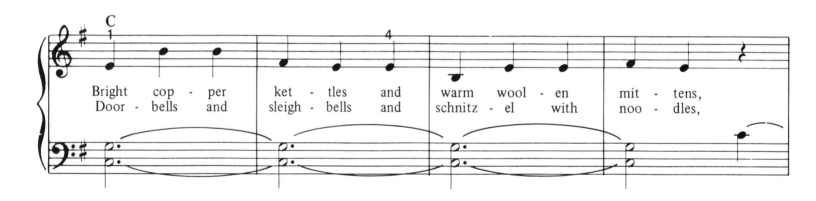

Bright cop - per ket - tles and warm wool - en mit - tens,
Door - bells and sleigh - bells and schnitz - el with noo - dles,

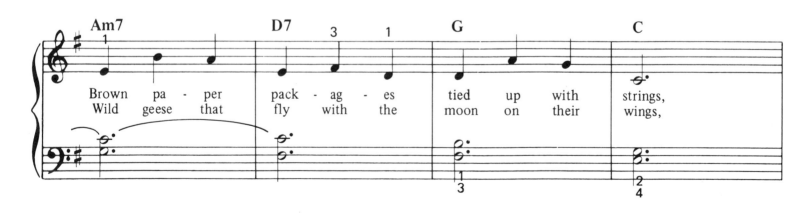

Brown pa - per pack - ag - es tied up with strings,
Wild geese that fly with the moon on their wings,

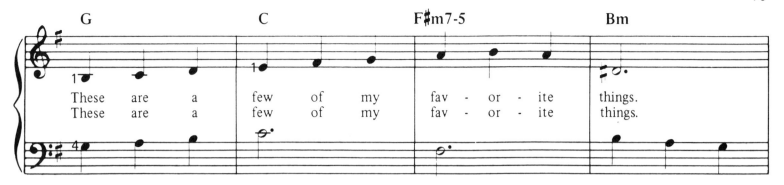

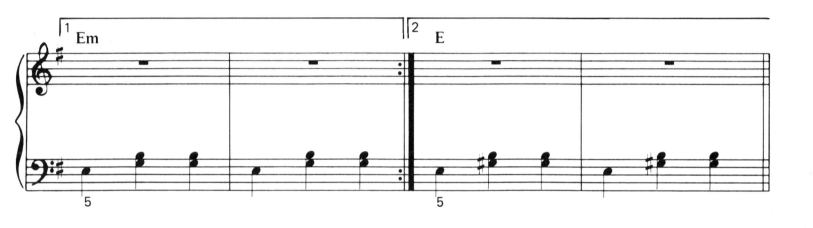

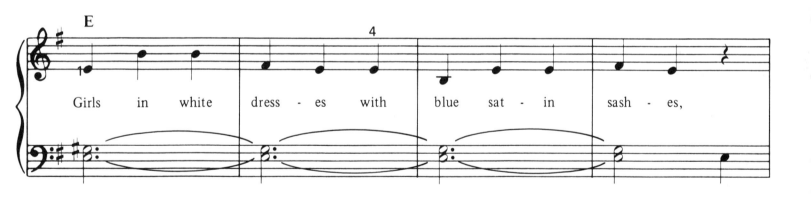

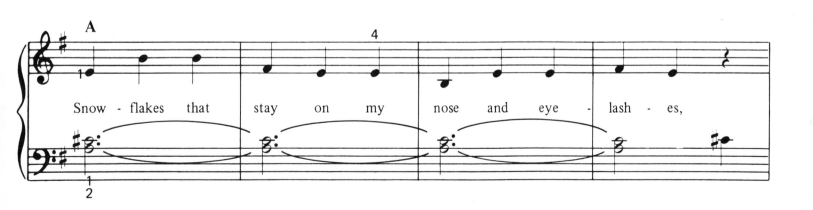

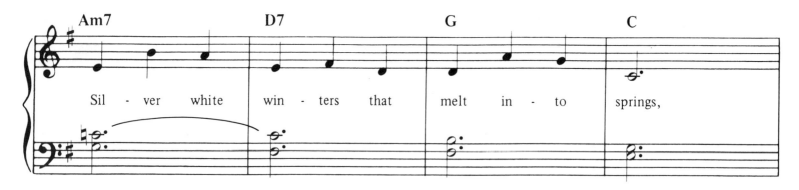

Am7   D7   G   C

Sil - ver white win - ters that melt in - to springs,

G   C   F#m7-5   B7

These are a few of my fav - or - ite things.

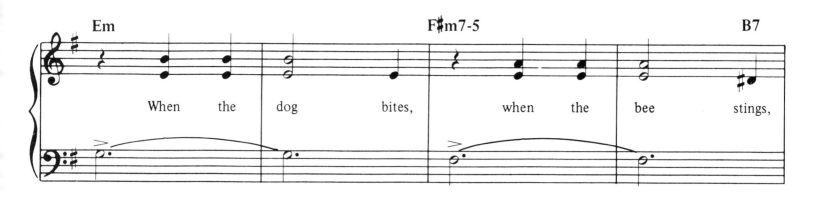

Em   F#m7-5   B7

When the dog bites, when the bee stings,

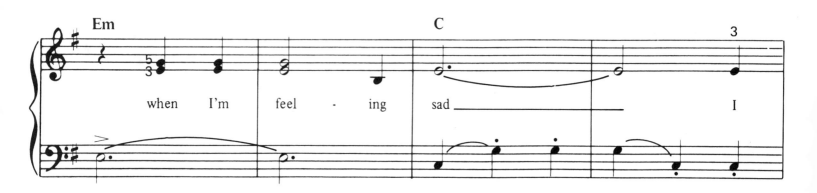

Em   C

when I'm feel - ing sad _____ I

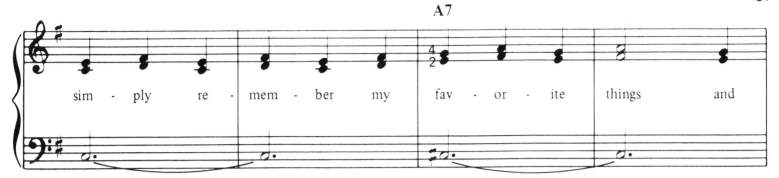

simply re- mem- ber my fav - or- ite things and

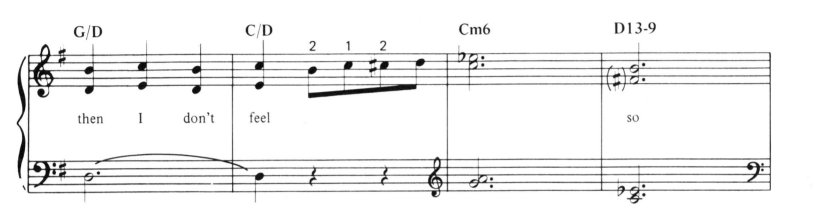

then I don't feel so

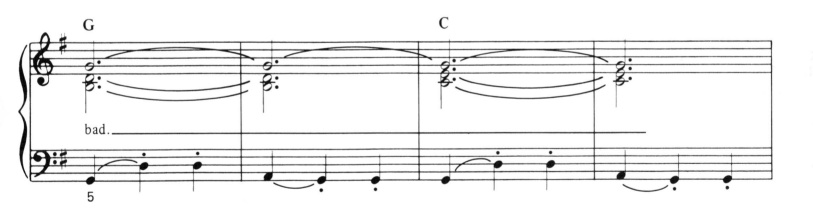

bad.

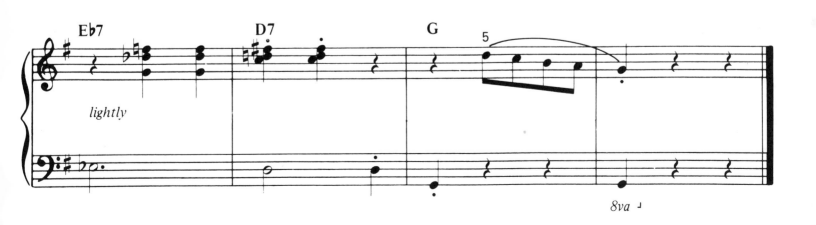

lightly

8va

PEOPLE WILL SAY WE'RE IN LOVE

from OKLAHOMA!

Lyrics by OSCAR HAMMERSTEIN II
Music by RICHARD RODGERS

With a lilt

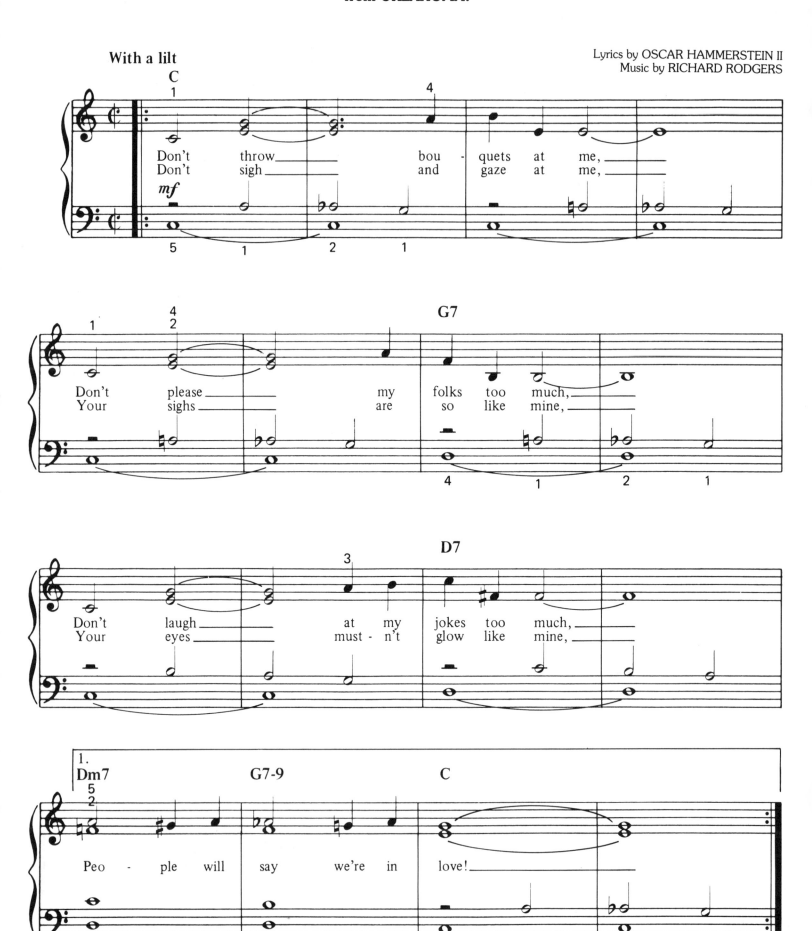

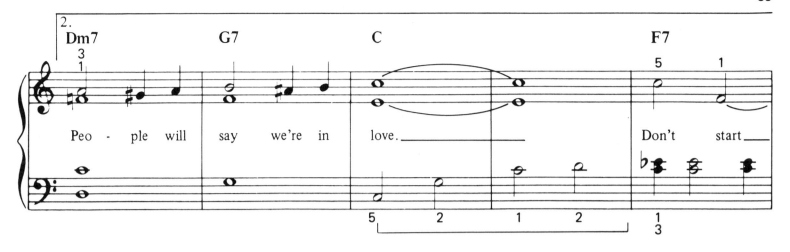

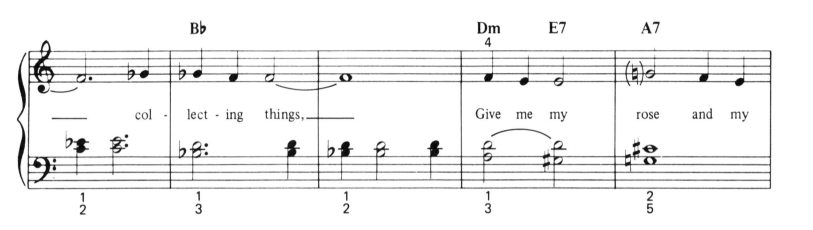

more deliberately

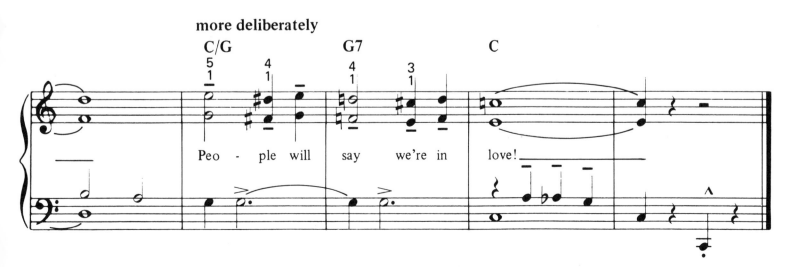

SOME ENCHANTED EVENING

from SOUTH PACIFIC

Lyrics by OSCAR HAMMERSTEIN II
Music by RICHARD RODGERS

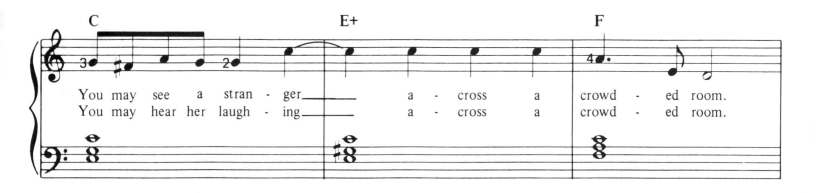

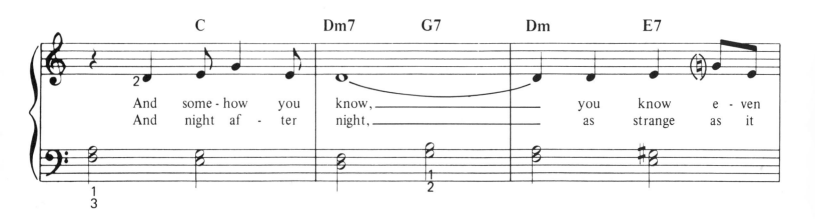

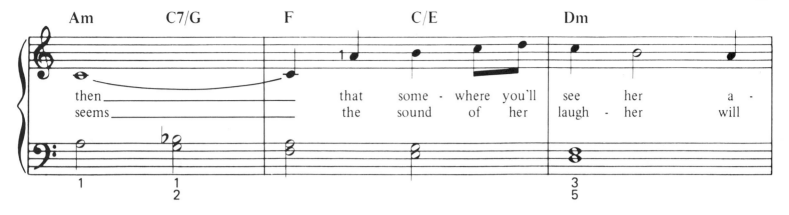

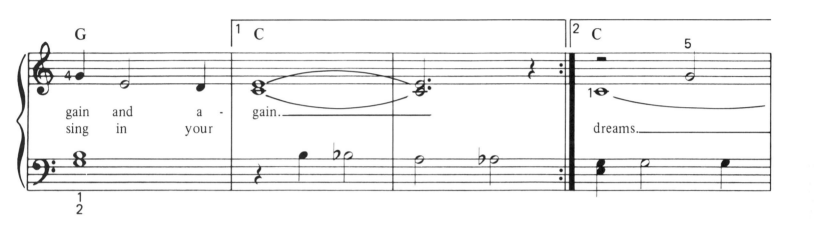

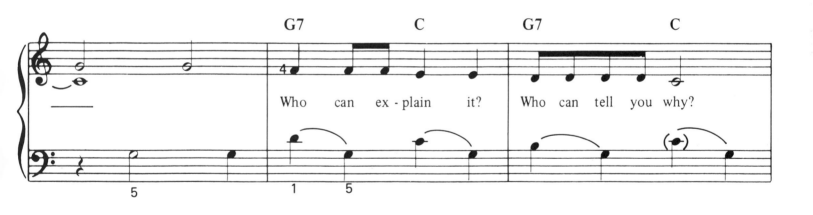

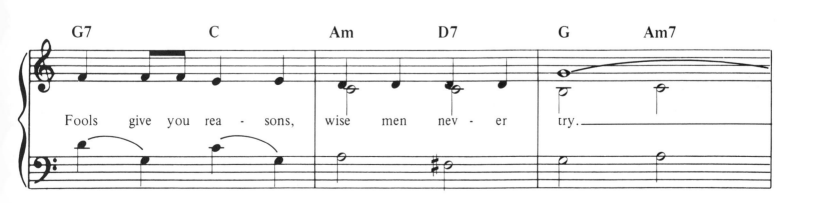

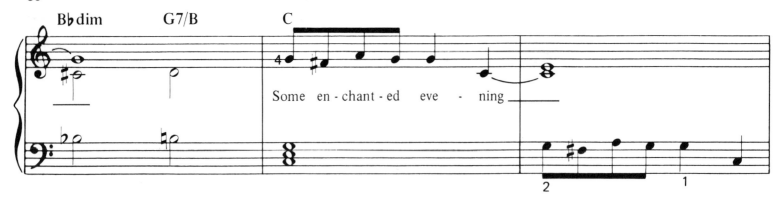

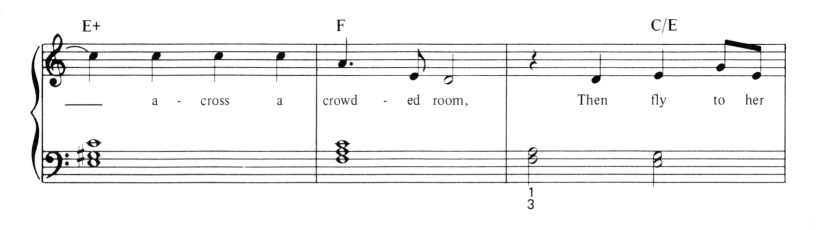

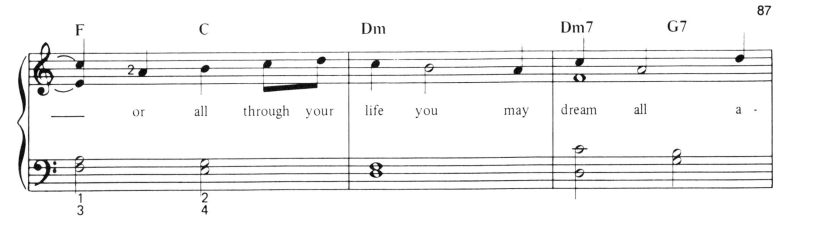

or all through your life you may dream all a-

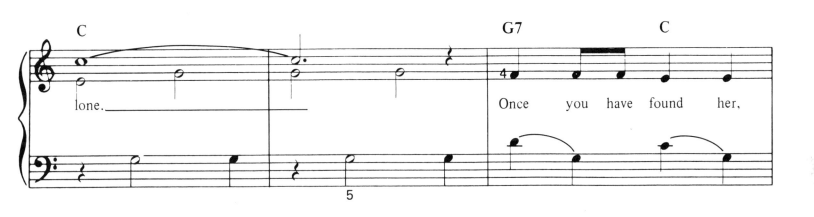

lone. Once you have found her,

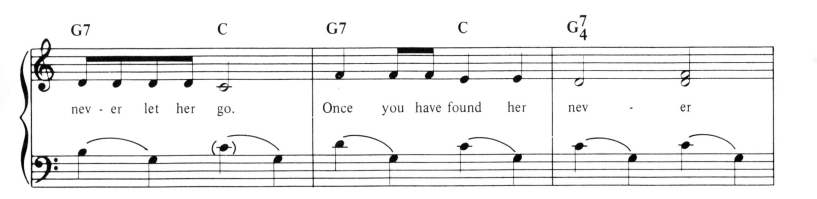

nev - er let her go. Once you have found her nev - er

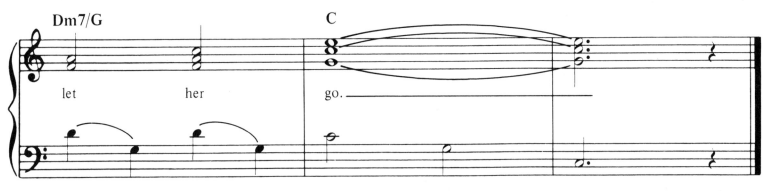

let her go.

THE SOUND OF MUSIC

from THE SOUND OF MUSIC

Lyrics by OSCAR HAMMERSTEIN II
Music by RICHARD RODGERS

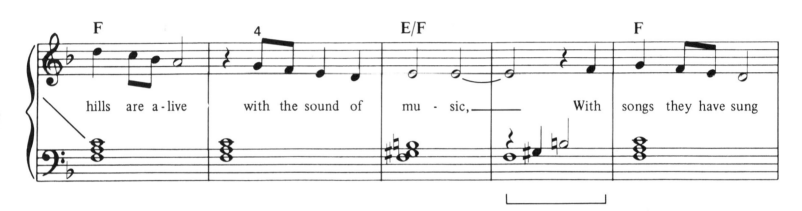

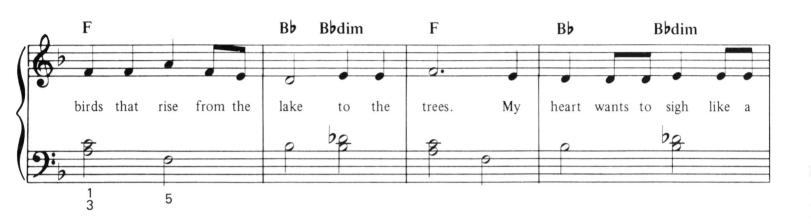

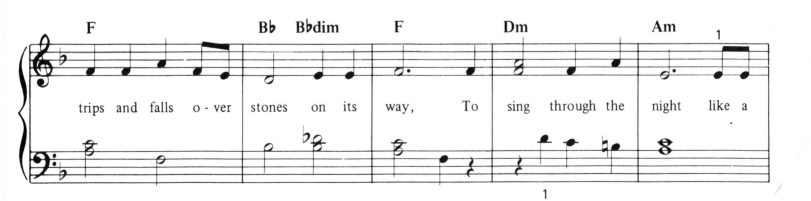

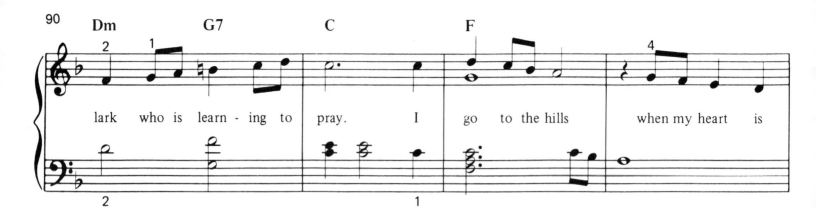

lark who is learn - ing to pray. I go to the hills when my heart is

lone - ly, _____ I know I will hear what I've heard be -

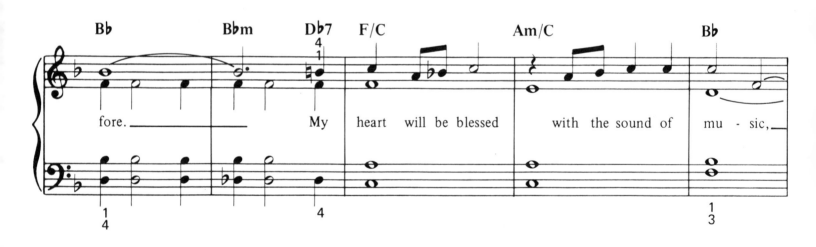

fore. _____ My heart will be blessed with the sound of mu - sic,

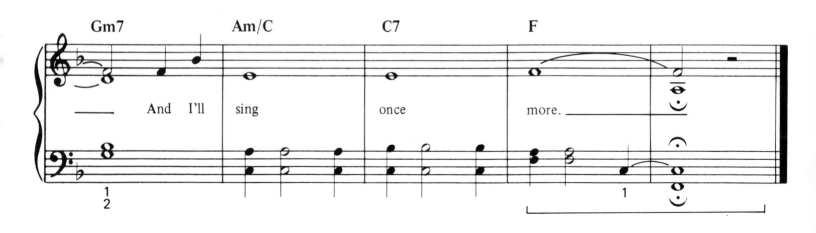

_____ And I'll sing once more. _____

TILL THERE WAS YOU
from Meredith Willson's THE MUSIC MAN

By MEREDITH WILLSON

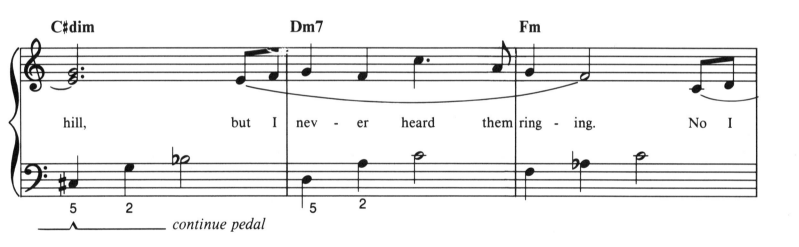

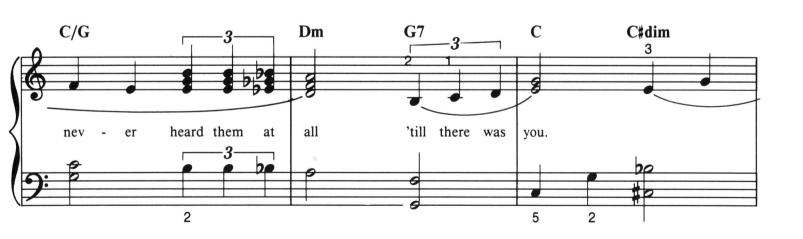

There were birds in the sky, but I

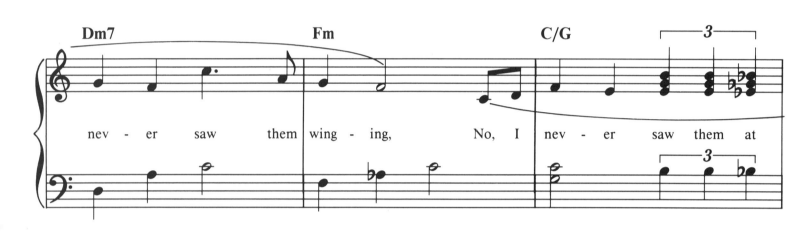

nev - er saw them wing - ing, No, I nev - er saw them at

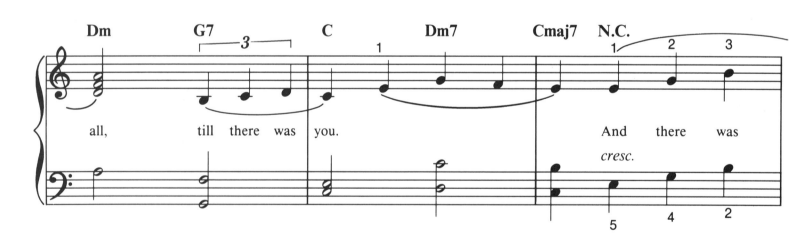

all, till there was you. And there was

cresc.

mu - sic and there were won - der - ful ro - ses, they

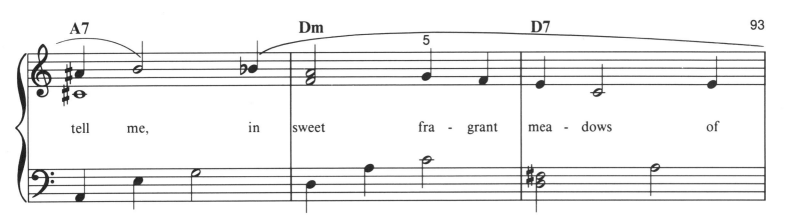

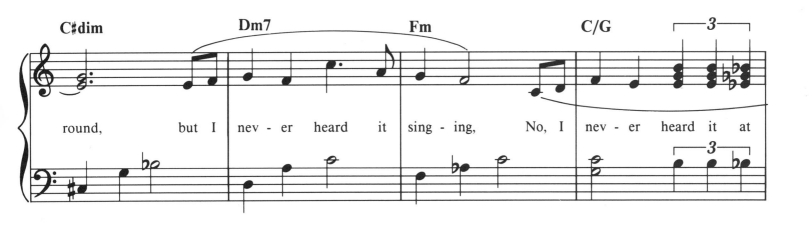

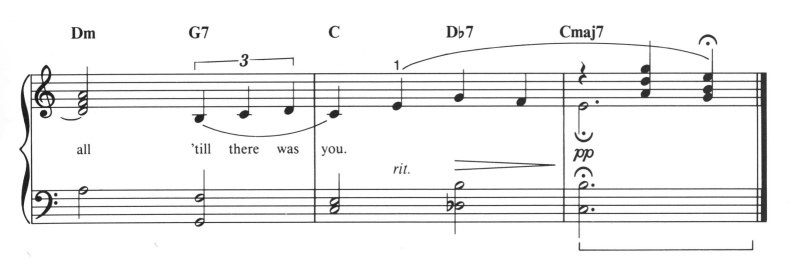

SUNRISE, SUNSET

from the Musical FIDDLER ON THE ROOF

Words by SHELDON HARNICK
Music by JERRY BOCK

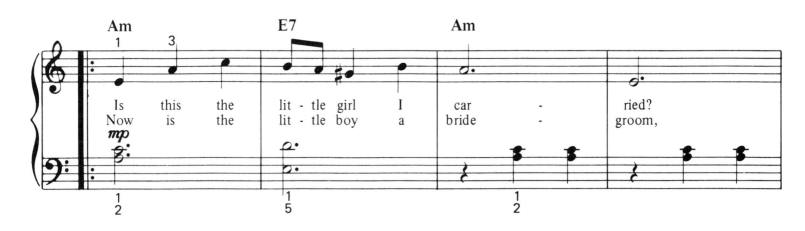

Is this the lit - tle girl I car - ried?
Now is the lit - tle boy a bride - groom,

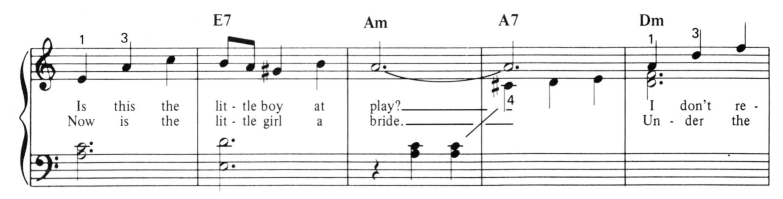

Is this the lit - tle boy at play?
Now is the lit - tle girl a bride.

I don't re -
Un - der the

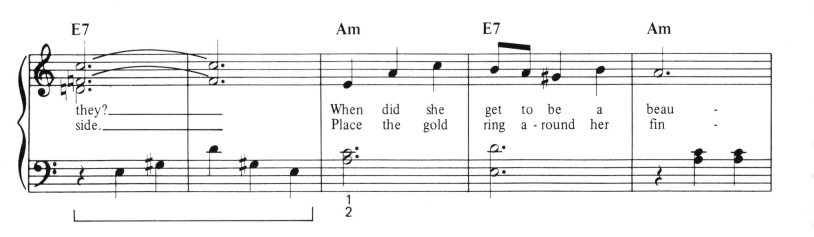

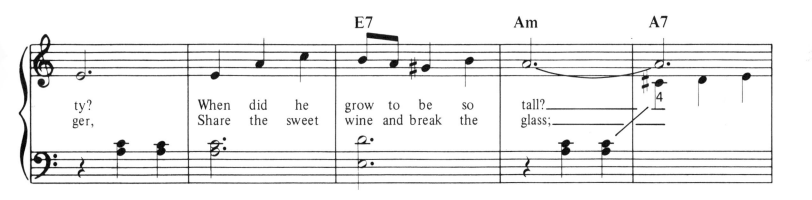

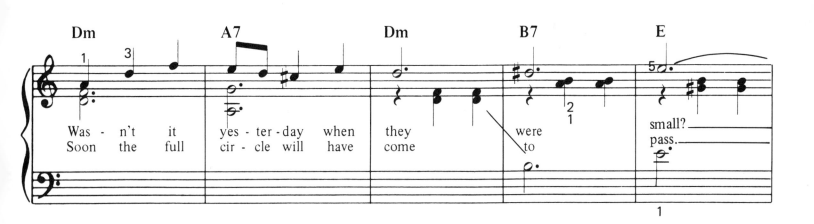

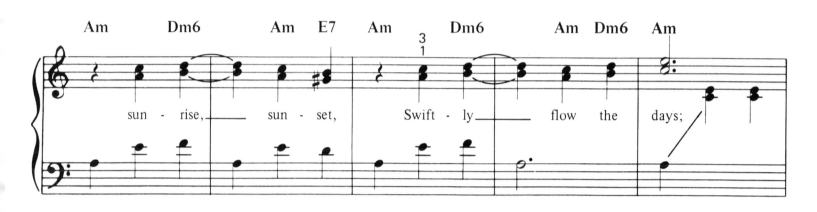

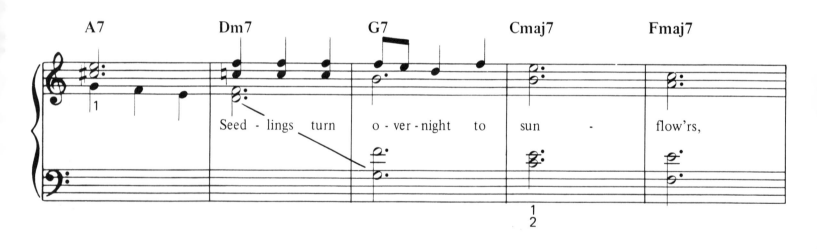

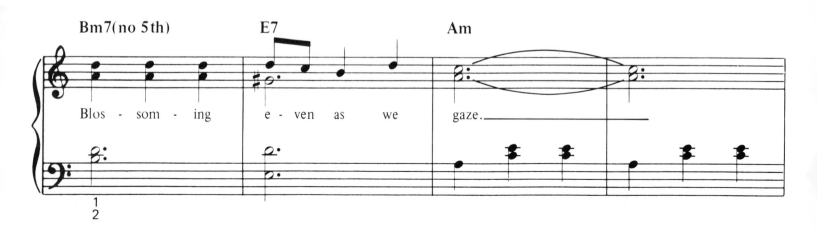

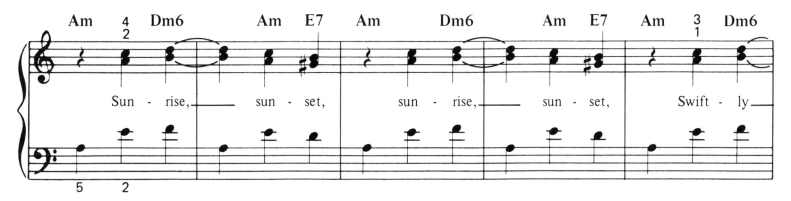

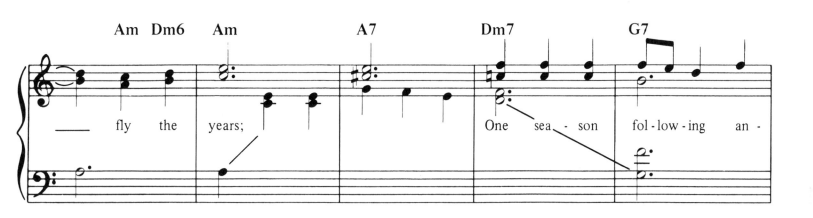

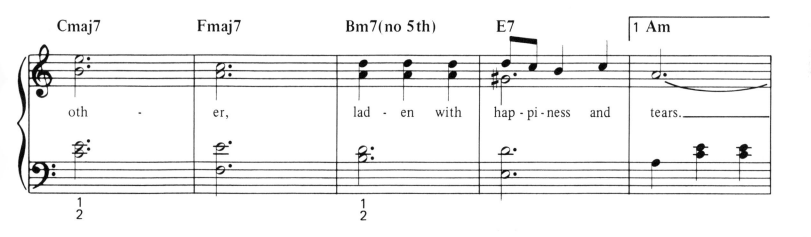

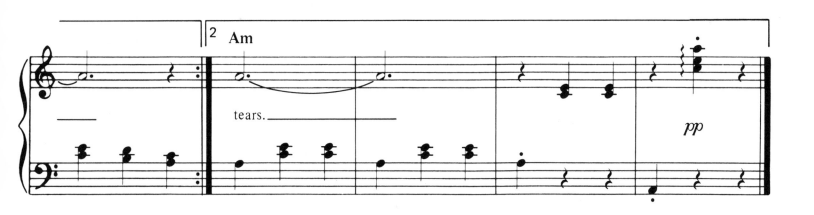

UNEXPECTED SONG
from SONG & DANCE

Music by ANDREW LLOYD WEBBER
Lyrics by DON BLACK

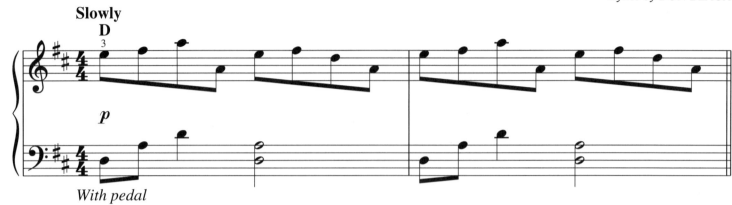

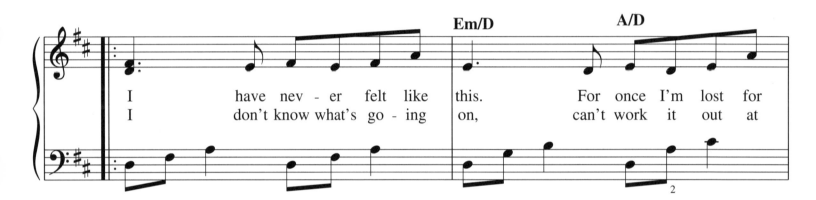

I have nev-er felt like this. For once I'm lost for

I don't know what's go-ing on, can't work it out at

words, your smile has real-ly thrown me. This is not like me at

all. What-ev-er made you choose me? I just can't be-lieve my

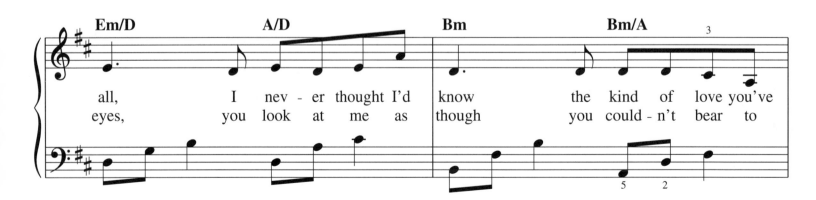

all, I nev-er thought I'd know the kind of love you've

eyes, you look at me as though you could-n't bear to

words, your smile has real - ly thrown me. This is not like me at

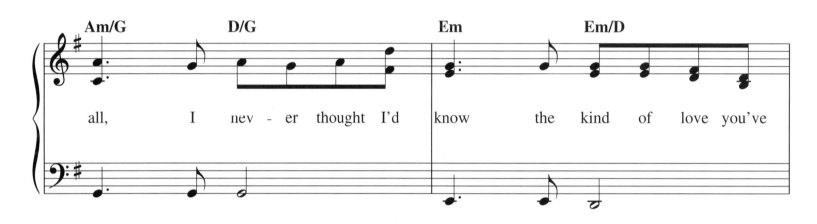

all, I nev - er thought I'd know the kind of love you've

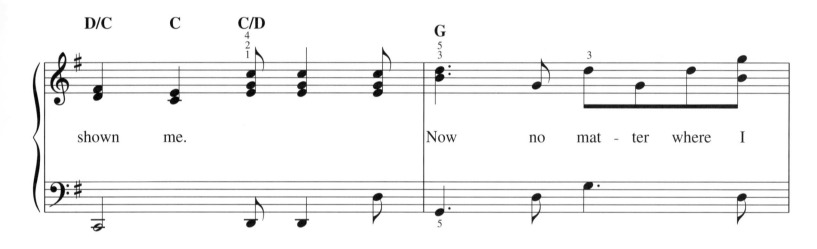

shown me. Now no mat - ter where I

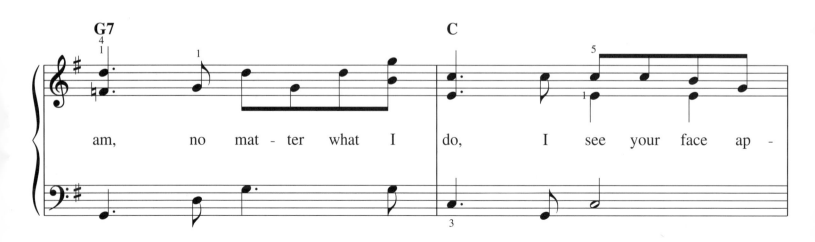

am, no mat - ter what I do, I see your face ap -